MATHEMATICS

Exploring Your World

THINKING CRITICALLY

Contributing Author

Dale Seymour

Developmental assistance by The Learning Source.

SILVER BURDETT & GINN

MORRISTOWN, NJ • NEEDHAM, MA

Atlanta, GA • Cincinnati, OH • Dallas, TX • Deerfield, IL • Menlo Park, CA

 ISBN 0-382-19694-5

THINKING CRITICALLY
Table of Contents/Scope and Sequence

Thinking Critically Masters	Related Student Pages	Attributes/Relationships	Decision Making/Planning	Logic	Number Sense/Numeration	Problem Solving	Visual Thinking
1	3–4						•
2	7–8				•		
3	11–12						•
4	13–14			•			
5	15–16					•	
6	19–20		•				
7	21–22						•
8	23–24						•
9	27–28	•					
10	41–42			•			
11	45–46						•
12	47–48	•					
13	51–52					•	
14	55–56				•		
15	57–58		•				
16	69–70	•					
17	71–72				•		
18	73–74			•			
19	79–80				•		
20	83–84					•	
21	85–86						•
22	87–88				•		
23	87–88					•	
24	99–100						•
25	101–102		•				
26	103–104				•		
27	105–106			•			
28	109–110	•					
29	113–114				•		
30	115–116		•				
31	117–118			•			
32	129–130	•					
33	131–132						•

Thinking Critically Masters	Related Student Pages	Attributes/Relationships	Decision Making/Planning	Logic	Number Sense/Numeration	Problem Solving	Visual Thinking
34	135–136					•	
35	139–140			•			
36	141–142						•
37	143–144		•				
38	143–144		•				
39	159–160	•					
40	161–162			•			
41	163–164						•
42	167–168		•				
43	169–170						•
44	171–172				•		
45	191–192				•		
46	193–194			•			
47	195–196					•	
48	201–202		•				
49	203–204	•					
50–51	207–208		•				
52	217–218			•			
53	219–220	•					
54	221–222				•		
55	225–226			•			
56	227–228		•				
57	229–230						•
58	233–234		•				
59	235–236			•			
60	237–238				•		
61	249–250						•
62	251–252						•
63	253–254	•					
64	255–256					•	
65	265–266			•			

Thinking Critically Masters	Related Student Pages	Attributes/Relationships	Decision Making/Planning	Logic	Number Sense/Numeration	Problem Solving	Visual Thinking
66	267–268			•			
67	269–270				•		
68	271–272						•
69	273–274				•		
70	275–276				•		
71	277–278		•				
72	289–290				•		
73	295–296				•		
74	297–298						•
75	299–300					•	
76	305–306			•			
77	309–310	•					
78	311–312		•				
79	327–328						•
80	329–330						•
81	333–334			•			
82	335–336					•	
83–84	339–340						•
85	349–350	•					
86	353–354						•
87	355–356				•		
88	357–358			•			
89	359–360	•					
90	363–364				•		
91	367–368						•
92	369–370				•		
93	371–372		•				
94	385–386				•		
95	387–388	•					
96	393–394					•	
97	395–396		•				

TO THE TEACHER

The teaching of critical thinking skills has become an integral part of the school curriculum. The activities in *Thinking Critically* provide students with an opportunity to use a wide range of thinking skills that extend and apply the mathematics concepts developed in Silver Burdett & Ginn's **MATHEMATICS: Exploring Your World.**

Benefits

The activities in *Thinking Critically* can help students in these ways.

- Students develop the ability to analyze and synthesize information needed for solving problems and making decisions. To be a good problem solver, a student must have a command of basic thinking skills.
- The activities expand and enhance the growth of problem-solving skills. Problem solving involves more than applying the previously learned computation skills. Many of the activities in *Thinking Critically* require students to analyze and to evaluate pictorial or textual information and then apply a process to find a solution.
- The activities encourage independent thinking and provide opportunities for reflective and divergent thinking. This creative thinking encourages the use of alternate methods of solution.
- The activities foster cooperative learning skills in a problem-solving environment. Many activities suggest that students work with a partner or in a small group as they solve a problem.

Topics in Thinking Critically

Visual Thinking Many of the visual thinking activities involve recognition of transformations, rotations, symmetry, and whole/part relationships. The basic thinking skills of comparing and contrasting are applied in the activities as are many problem-solving strategies.

Attributes and Relationships In these lessons students continue a visual or number pattern, classify objects, and create a new situation that follows a set of rules discovered in the initial exploration.

Logic and Deductive Reasoning Using reasoning skills to solve a puzzle is one type of logic activity. Students also analyze a series of statements and eliminate impossibilities in order to reach a conclusion.

Number Sense/Numeration The activities in this category include the following: organized counting; place value concepts; estimating; probability; interpreting and creating graphs, tables, and charts; collecting and organizing data; evaluating statistics; and judging the validity of generalizations.

Decision Making/Planning Simulations of real-life situations give students experience with decision-making and planning processes. The activities include experience with ordering events or steps in a process and with making purchasing and scheduling decisions.

Problem Solving The problem-solving lessons reflect many of the features of the problem solving strand in **MATHEMATICS: Exploring Your World.** Activities may require students to identify one or more strategies that can be used to solve a problem, to identify extraneous or missing information, to create problems with a given set of data, or to draw pictures or use manipulatives. Students are encouraged to explore different methods for solving a problem, and to realize that some problems have more than one solution. Encourage students to discuss their solutions. Through discussion students hear how others approach problem solving and they have a chance to refine and expand their language and thinking skills. Talking through their solutions and listening to others also helps them acquire more confidence in their own ability to solve problems. Students will perceive themselves as good problem solvers if they experience success.

The cooperative learning projects in *Thinking Critically* foster creative responses and require students to apply a wide range of skills. They often draw upon knowledge from other curriculum areas such as art, science, social studies, and language arts. You can encourage students to modify these projects to fit their interests, abilities, and needs.

Cooperative Learning

The activities in *Thinking Critically* provide many opportunities for cooperative learning in the classroom. Directions often suggest working with a partner or in a small group. The projects afford opportunities for developing and practicing some cooperative learning strategies and skills. You may wish to discuss the following cooperative learning practices that can enable students to work together more effectively and to successfully complete an activity.

- Listen to each other carefully.
- Help others understand what they are to do.
- Talk quietly and do not disturb other groups.
- Give everyone a chance to share ideas.
- Keep a record of your work.

Informal Assessment

Student responses to the *Thinking Critically* activities may be used to help assess their understanding of mathematics concepts. When students are given the opportunity to work on more challenging activities, you can often detect how well they have generalized concepts and can apply them to new situations. Students' responses can also be used to guide the growth of their thinking skills.

You may wish to use the following as a guide to help to evaluate a student's responses to an activity.

- Does the student give evidence of understanding the given situation? (You may want to ask students to demonstrate their understanding of a situation with a drawing or manipulatives.)
- Does the student attempt alternate solutions?
- Do the student's responses reflect divergent thinking at appropriate times? (Provide some ***What if*** questions that foster divergent thinking and alternate solutions.)
- For project lessons, did students follow the directions and reflect some appropriate creativity in their drawings and constructions?

You may want to duplicate a copy of the table of contents for each student and then use the cells of the scope and sequence section for recording your assessment of a student's work. Create your own code for recording achievement or you might use the following.

S — Satisfactorily completed
\+ — Outstanding or exceptional responses
MG — More guidance needed

You may want to have the students keep all or some of their completed work in a notebook. Encourage students to discuss their progress and how well they work independently and within a group.

Name ______________________________ **Visual Thinking**

Use with text pages 3–4.

Follow the Dots

1. Copy the picture.
   Start at the lines given.

2. Make your own picture.
   Ask a partner to copy it.

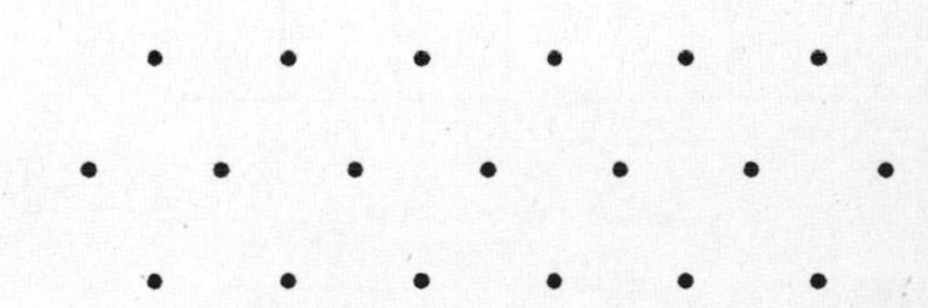

FOCUS: Students use visual thinking to copy images.

Name ______________________________ **Number Sense**

Use with text pages 7–8.

Collections

Which pile will fill the box with none left over? Make a guess. Ring the pile.

1\. 

2\. 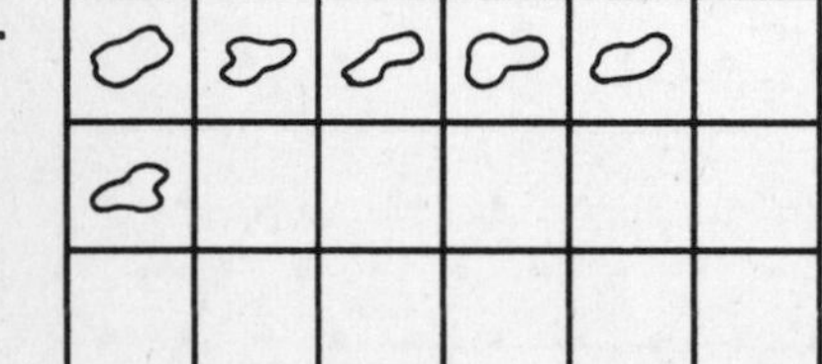 

3\. 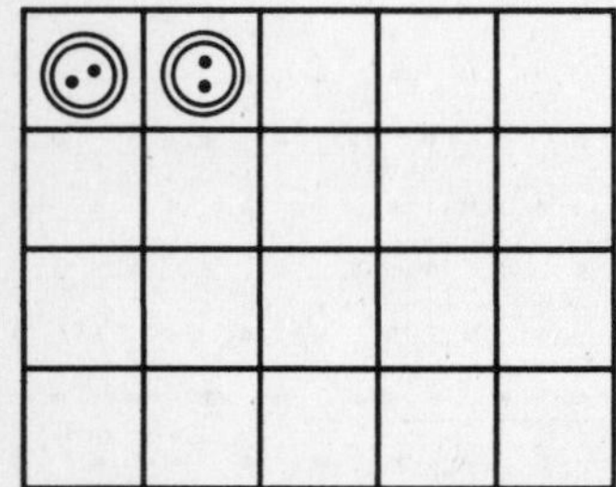 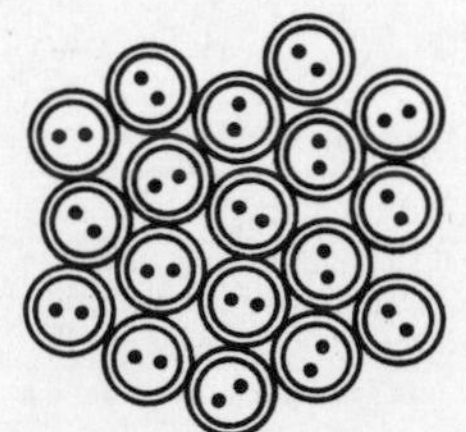  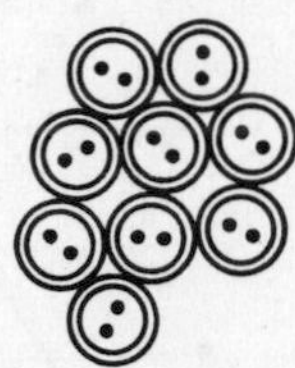

4\.   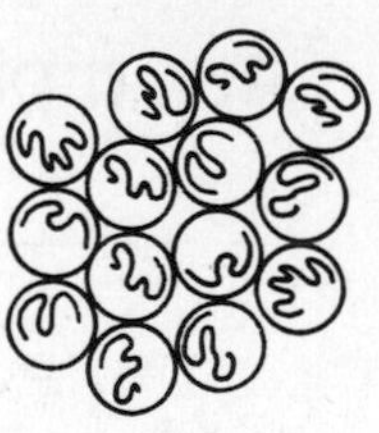

Share

Tell how you can check your answers.

FOCUS: Students use number sense to choose the pile of objects that will fill each box.

Name ____ **Visual Thinking**

Use with text pages 11–12.

Picture This!

Maria folded each piece of paper once. Then she cut out a shape on the fold. What will the shape look like when she unfolds the paper? Draw the missing part. One is done for you.

1. 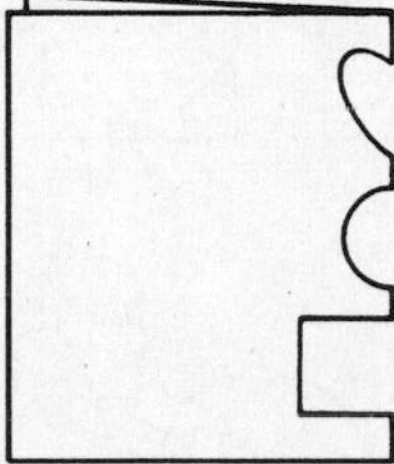

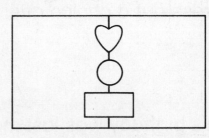

2. 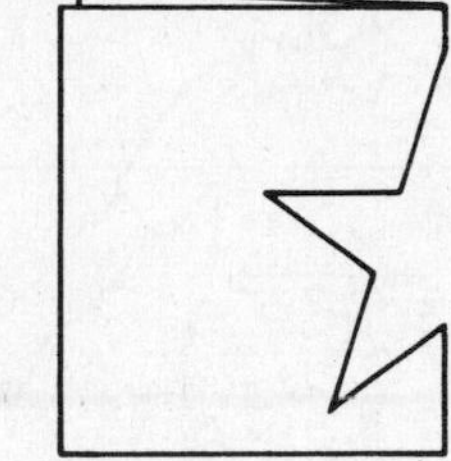 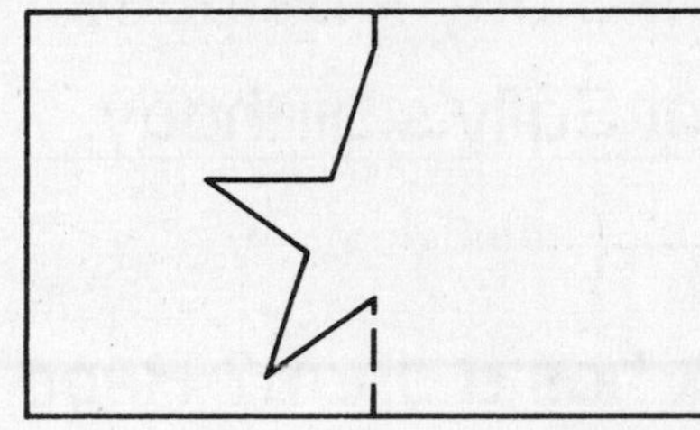

3.  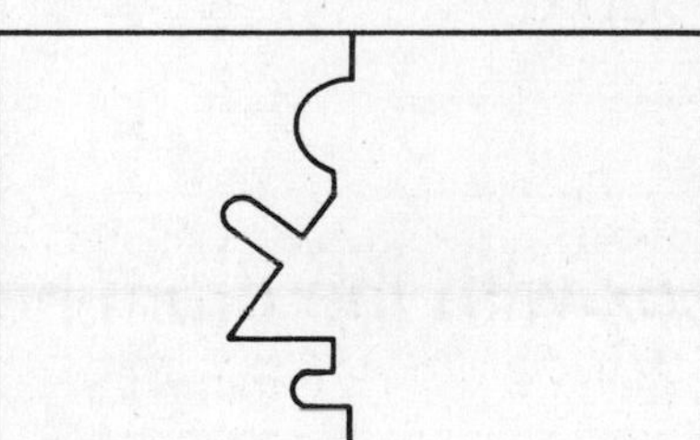

Draw the whole figure that you will see.

4. 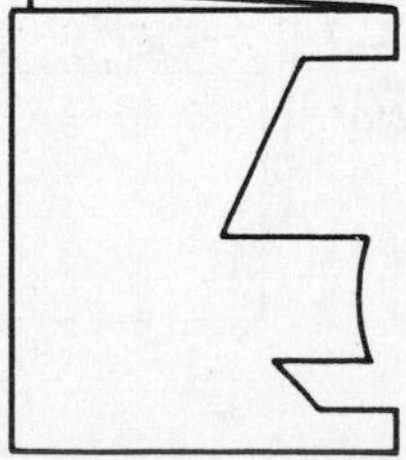 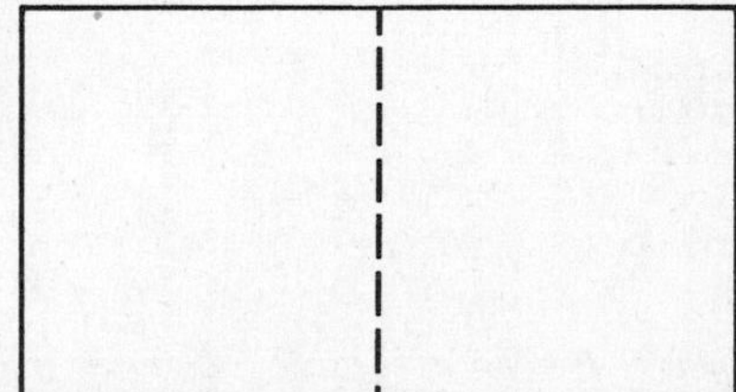

FOCUS: Students use mental imagery to complete symmetrical figures.

Happy Birthday to ?

Charlie, Jane, Sam, Pam, and Sally are at a birthday party. Who's birthday is it? Read the clues. Draw a party hat on the birthday child.

HINT Cross out a choice after you read a clue.

Clues

- Pam's birthday was last month.
- It is not a boy's birthday.
- It is not Sally's birthday.

Which box has a drum? Read the clues. Color that box.

Clues

- The box with the drum has stripes or dots.
- The box with the drum has a bow.
- The box with the drum is not in front of a girl.

FOCUS: Students use deductive reasoning to solve logic puzzles.

Puzzle Power

Talk about the kind of picture that would make a good puzzle. Check one.

- ☐ one little picture in each box
- ☐ one big picture that covers the whole grid

Why did you choose this kind of picture?

Make a puzzle. Draw a picture on the grid. Cut out the pieces on the dark lines. Have a partner put the puzzle back together.

FOCUS: Students use visual thinking to create and complete puzzles.

Name ____

Visual Thinking

Use with text pages 23–24.

Building Blocks

How many blocks must you add or take away to make the wall in the box?

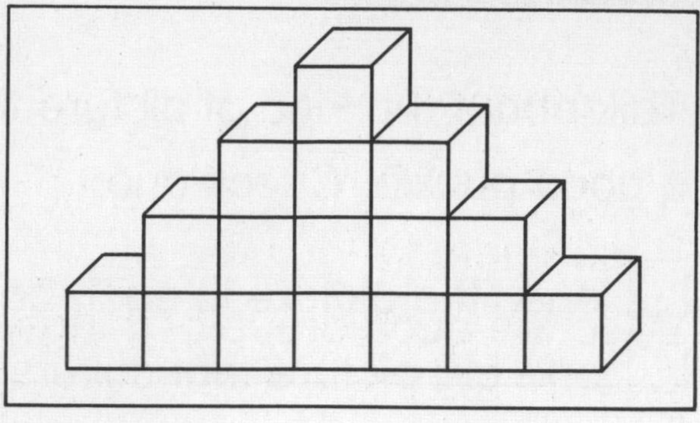

HINT Build with cubes to help.

1\.

Take away _____ .

Add _____ .

2\.

Take away _____ .

Add _____ .

3\.

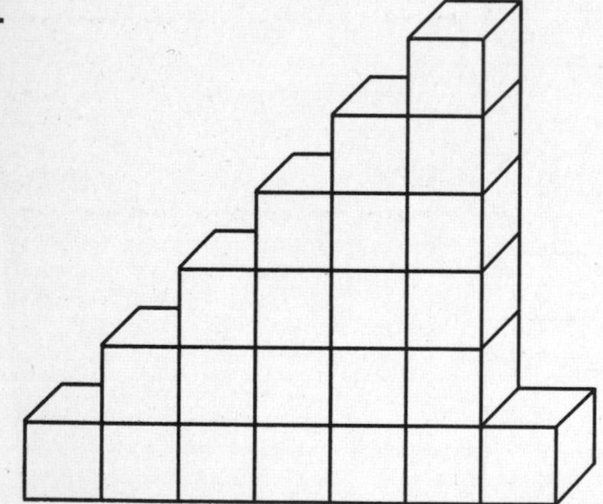

Take away _____ .

Add _____ .

4\.

Take away _____ .

Add _____ .

FOCUS: Students identify the number of missing or extra blocks that are in a structure.

Name ____

Yard Sale

Cut out the pictures along the dotted lines.

Think about how to sort the things.

Paste them in the boxes.

Describe each group of things.

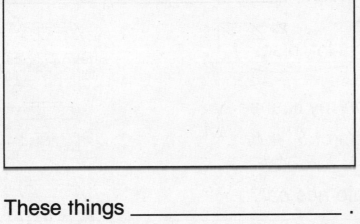

These things ____________________ .

These things ____________________ .

screwdriver 10¢
glue 15¢
pad 15¢
nails 10¢
tape 10¢
pencil 10¢
scissors 15¢
string 10¢
stapler 15¢
hammer 15¢

Share

Tell a classmate how you sorted the things.

FOCUS: Students classify objects according to groups that they create.

Name ______________________________ **Logic**

Use with text pages 41–42.

Four Little Pigs

Help the pigs find their cars.

Draw a line to match.

My license plate has letters and numbers.

My car is in this lot, also.

The number on my license plate is the sum of 6 + 6.

My license plate has only letters.

Match each pig with its house.

My house is on this street.

The number on my house is the sum of 4 + 5.

My house does not have a chimney.

My house is not made of bricks.

FOCUS: Students use deductive reasoning and their knowledge of addition to solve logic problems.

Name ________________________________

Toy Factory

Help the people in the toy factory. Tell how many buttons they need to make the animals. Fill in the chart.

HINT You may want to draw a picture, use counters, or use patterns.

Bunny Rabbits	Buttons
1	
2	
3	
4	

Teddy Bears	Buttons
1	
2	
3	
4	

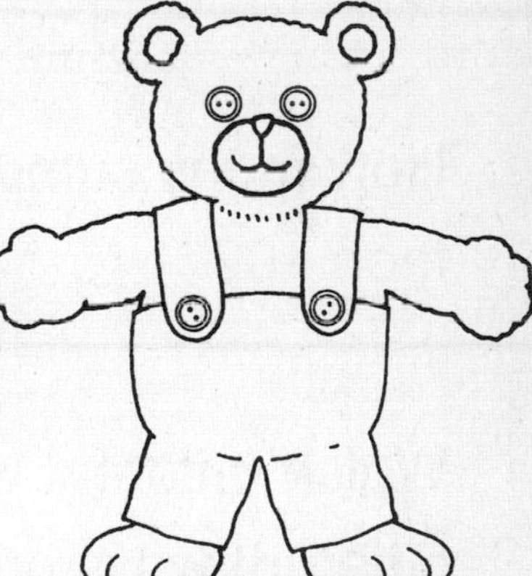

Share

Tell how you found the answers.

FOCUS: Students solve problems by using computational skills, drawing pictures, using counters, or using number patterns.

Name ______________________________ **Number Sense**

Use with text pages 55–56.

Tossing for Tens

Work with a partner. Toss two number cubes that show 1, 2, 3, 4, 5, and 6. Find the sum of the two numbers that come up. Do this 10 times.

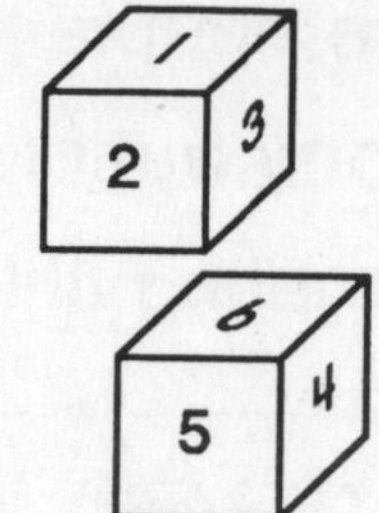

1. First, guess which will come up more often. Ring your answer.

   a sum of less than 10

   a sum greater than 10

Toss to find out. Fill in the chart as you toss the cubes. The first space shows the sum of the cubes above.

Toss	Try	1	2	3	4	5	6	7	8	9	10
Sum	1 + 6 7										

2. How many sums were less than 10? _____

3. How many sums were 10 or greater? _____

4. Which different ways can the sum 7 come up? Show the different ways on the chart.

Cube 1	1	6	2			
Cube 2	6	1	5			

FOCUS: Students do a probability experiment and record their results in a chart.

Name ______________________________________ **Decision Making**

Use with text pages 57–58.

Fair Play

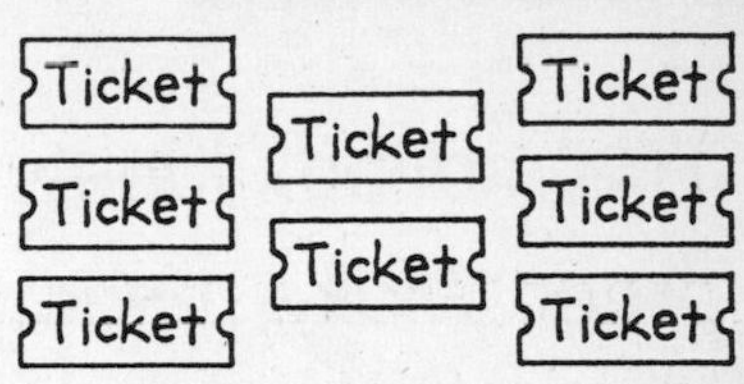

Welcome to the Fair. Find 4 different ways to use exactly 8 tickets. Write letters to show each choice. One is done for you.

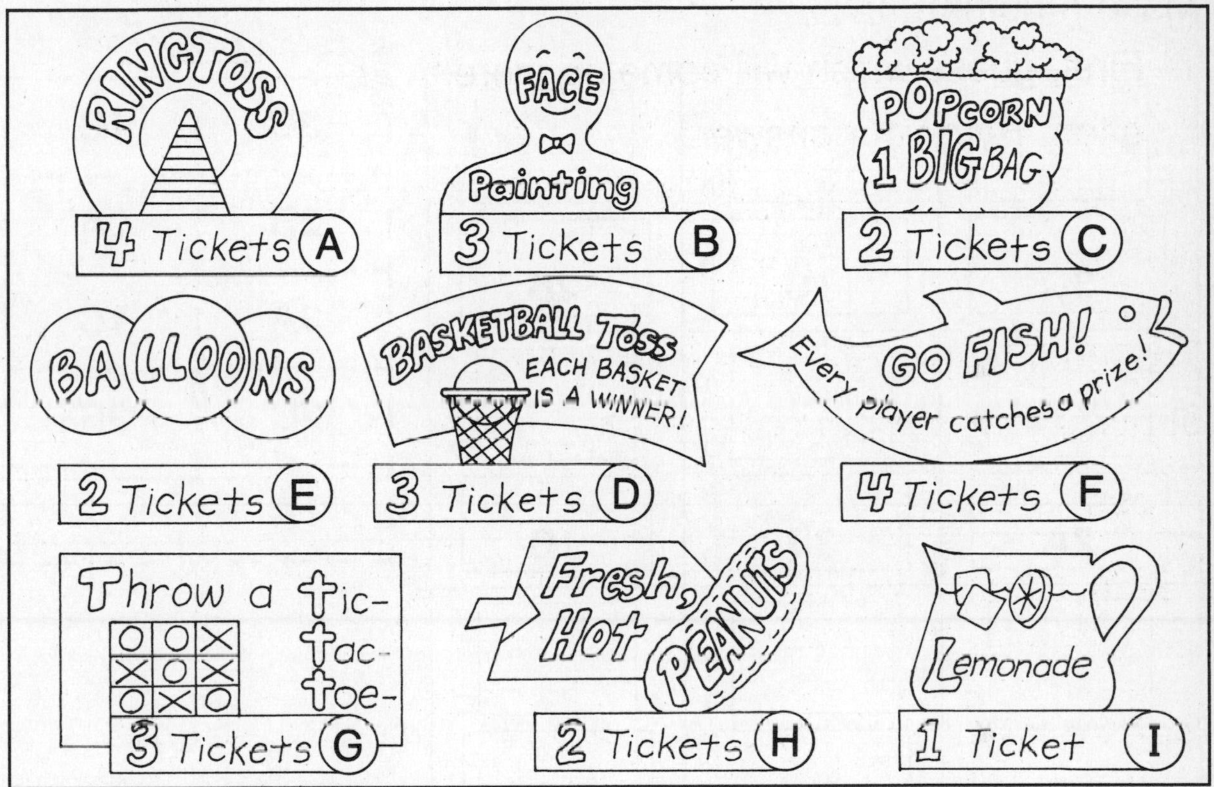

Choice 1

B, D, E

Choice 2

____

Choice 3

____

Choice 4

____

Ring the choice that you like best.

FOCUS: Students use their knowledge of addition and subtraction to make purchasing decisions.

Mail Mix-up

The mailbox labels are not in a good order. Make the letter carrier's job easier. Paste the new labels over the old ones. Make a pattern.

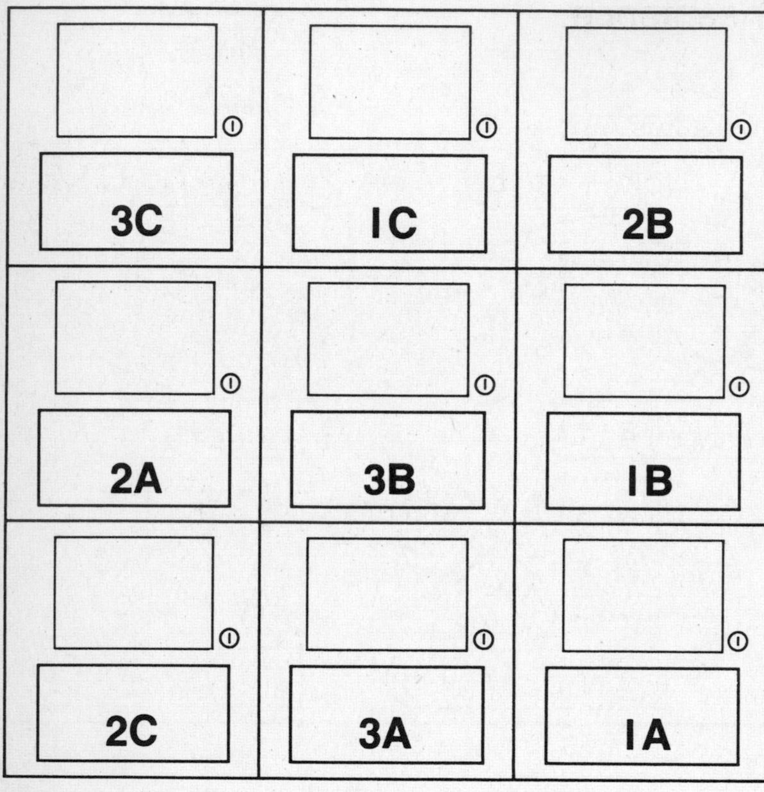

3C	1B
2B	2A
3A	1C
2C	3B
1A	

Share

Compare your work with a classmate's work. Did you order the labels in the same way? Did you both make the letter carrier's job easier?

FOCUS: Students organize labels in a useful way.

Name ______________________________

Eyes Shut

What if you took one marble out of the box with your eyes shut? Ring the kind of marble that you would be most likely to pick.

1. 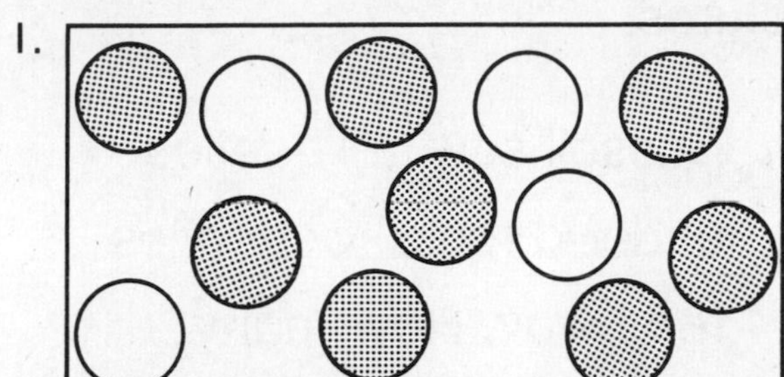 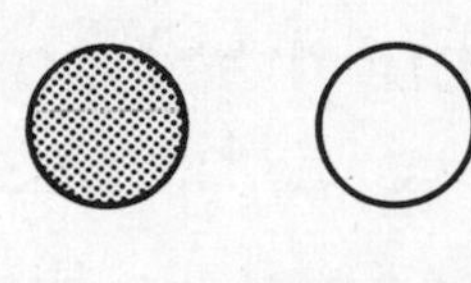

2. 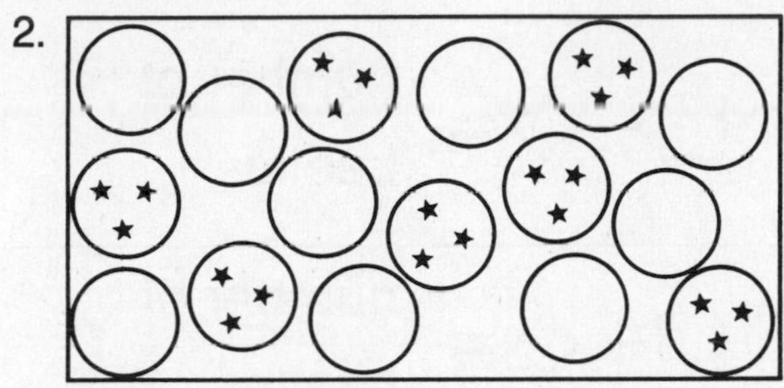 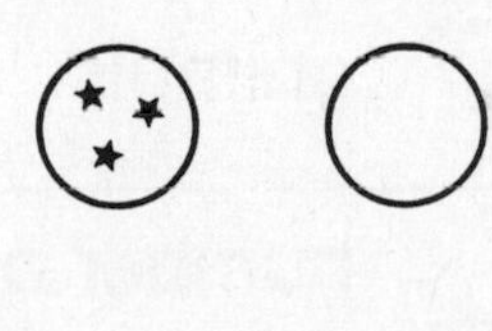

3. 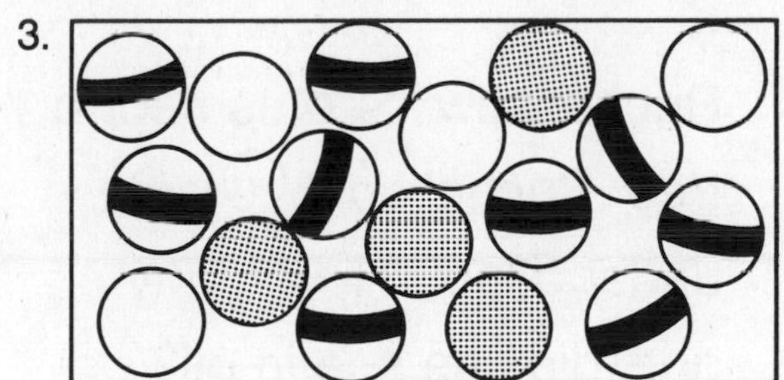 

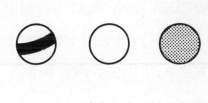

4. 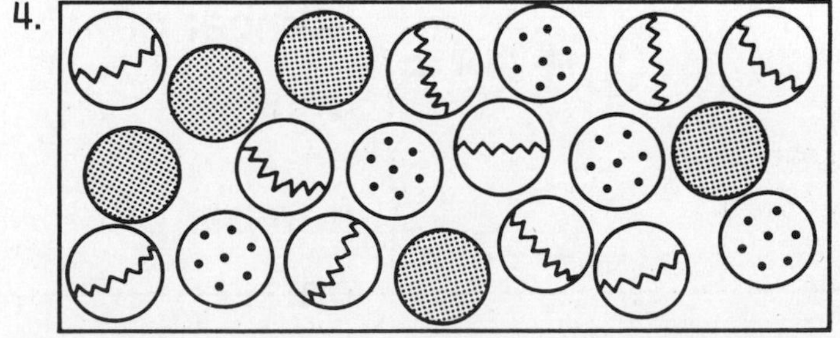 

FOCUS: Students determine the probability of randomly selecting an object.

Name ______________________________ **Problem Solving**
Use with text pages 83–84.

Creep, Crawl, or Fly

Read the problem. Ring the sentence that tells about it.

Use numbers in place of pictures.

1. Rachel saw △ cows. Russell saw ○ horses. How many animals did Rachel and Russell see?

   △ + ○ = number of animals

   △ − ○ = number of animals

2. Russell saw □ beetles under a rock. ◇ beetles ran away. How many beetles were left?

   □ − ◇ = number of beetles

   □ + ◇ = number of beetles

3. Rachel counted ☆ slugs. ✿ slugs went away. How many slugs were left?

   ☆ − ✿ = number of slugs

   ✿ − ☆ = number of slugs

4. Rachel saw ☾ ants near a tree. Rachel saw ⊙ ants under a leaf. How many ants did she see in all?

   ☾ + ⊙ = number of ants

   ☾ − ⊙ = number of ants

FOCUS: Students select a number sentence that represents a mathematical relationship in a word problem.

Microscope Math

Tricia put the numbers 1 through 9, which she found in an old book, under her microscope. Write each number under its part. (None of the numbers are turned.)

HINT First, do the numbers that you are sure of.

1. 
____

2. 
____

3. 
____

4. 
____

5. 
____

6. 
____

7. 
____

8. 
____

9. 
____

FOCUS: Students use visual thinking to match a part of a numeral to its whole.

Name ____________________ **Number Sense/Project**

Use with text pages 87–88.
Use masters 22 and 23.

Ready, Set, Grow

Planting Seeds

Read this problem.

One plant is kept in the light. One plant is kept in a dark place, such as a closet. Which one will have a longer stem?

Ring your guess. the plant in the light

the plant in the dark

Work in a small group to find the answer. Follow these steps.

1. Soak 4 lima beans in water overnight.

2. Get 2 clear plastic containers. Fill both containers with wet cotton or paper towels.
3. Place 2 lima beans in each container. Place the beans on the side of the container. That way you can see them grow.
4. Put one container in the light. Label it with the letter L. Put the other in the dark. Label it with the letter D.
5. Keep the cotton or paper towels wet.

FOCUS: Students set up a plant experiment.

Use with text pages 87–88.
Use masters 22 and 23 together.

Ready, Set, Grow!

Measuring the Growth

Measure the stem of each plant on days 3, 6, and 9. Use a red ribbon to measure the plant grown in the light. Use a blue ribbon to measure the one kept in the dark. Cut each ribbon as long as each stem that you are measuring. Tape each ribbon on the table. The letter L stands for the plant grown in the light. The letter D stands for the plant that you kept in the dark.

HEIGHTS OF PLANTS					
Day 3		Day 6		Day 9	
L	D	L	D	L	D

L = Light D = Dark

Share

After day 9, talk about what you see. Which stem is longer? Tell why you think this happened.

____

FOCUS: Students do an experiment to determine the better conditions for plant growth and to measure plants to the nearest whole centimeter.

Note: Each student group will need two clear plastic containers, four lima beans, cotton or paper towels, some red ribbon and blue ribbon, scissors, tape, and water. (Stripes of colored paper may be used instead of ribbons.) Have each group label its containers. (Do not put plants in direct sunlight.)

Name ____ **Visual Thinking**

Use with text pages 99–100.

Ins and Outs

Look at each pond. Find the fish.

Draw three more fish in each pond.

Draw two flowers outside each pond.

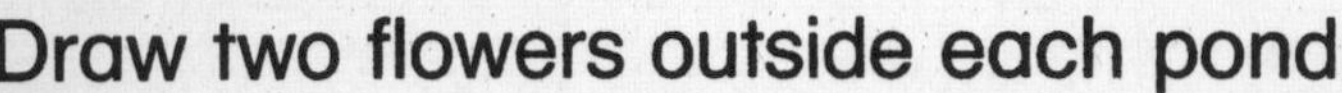

Color the pond if you need help.

1.

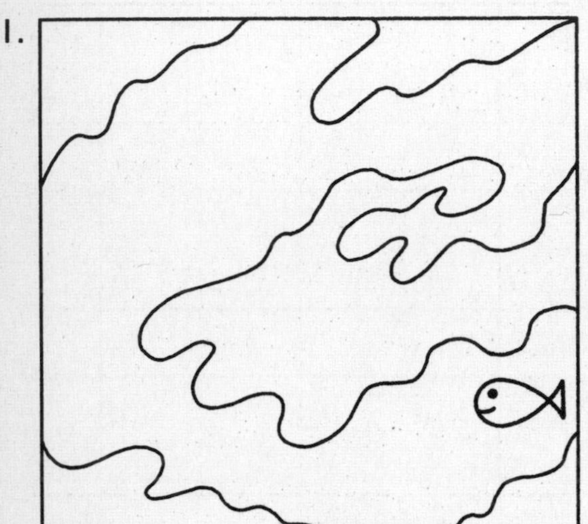

2.

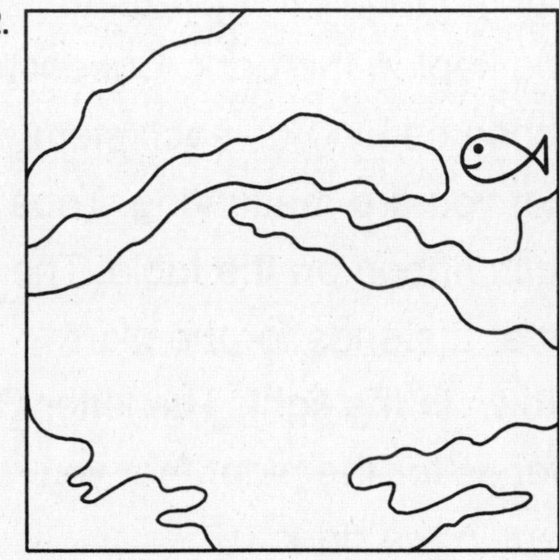

3.

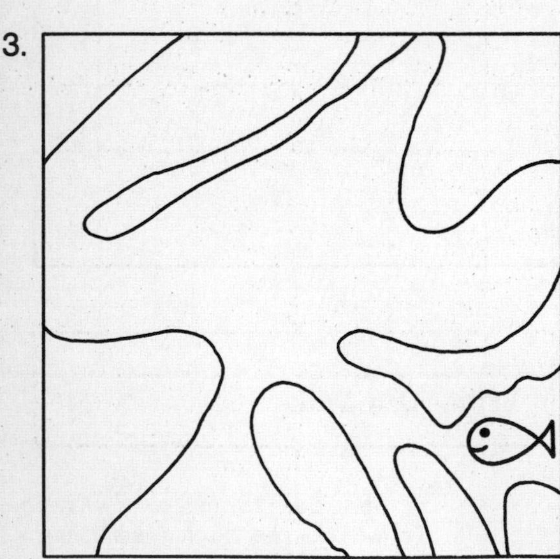

4.

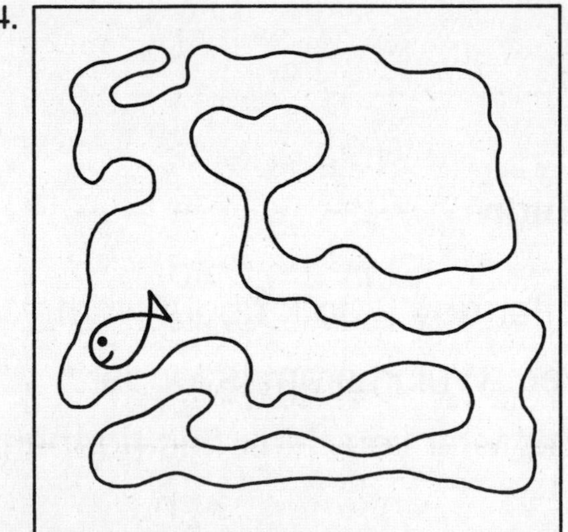

FOCUS: Students identify the inside and outside regions of figures.

Name ____________________ **Decision Making**

Use with text pages 101–102.

Greetings

How would you make a greeting card? Cut and paste to show the order. You may not want to use all these steps.

When you have finished, compare your charts. Does everyone have the same steps or the same order? Explain.

Make a picture

Fold the paper.

Get paper.

Get markers.

Write a note.

Sign the card.

Get crayon.

Make a design.

Paste the steps here.

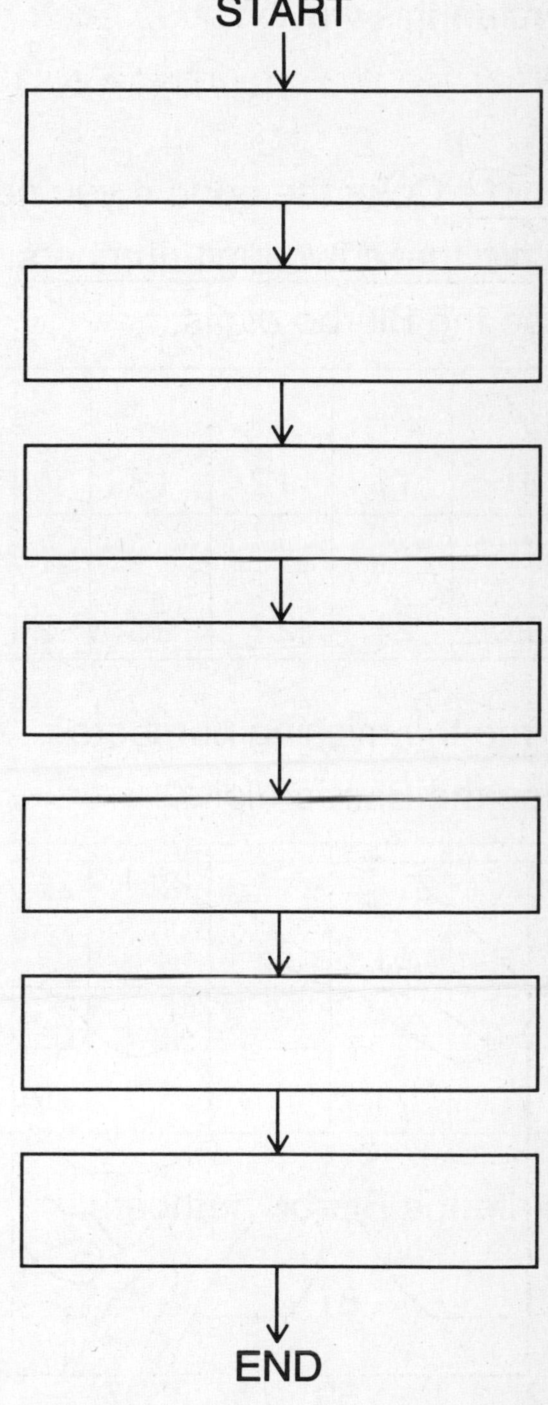

FOCUS: Students select and order steps in a process to make a simple flow chart.

Name ______________________________ **Number Sense**

Use with text pages 103–104.

Blurbo Numbers

On the Planet Blurbo the digits 0 to 9 are written this way:

⊙	—	=	ǂ	∧	△	≙	⍋	◇	⟠
0	1	2	3	4	5	6	7	8	9

Write these two-digit numbers.

Use the Blurbo digits.

10	— — 11	12	13	14	15	16	— ⍋ 17	18	19
20	= — 21	= = 22	23	24	25	26	27	= ◇ 28	29

Write the missing numbers.

Use the Blurbo digits.

≙ ⊙	≙ — 61	≙ =	≙ ǂ	≙ ∧	≙ △	≙ ≙	≙ ⍋	≙ ◇	≙ ⟠
⍋ ⊙ 70	⍋ — 71	⍋ =	⍋ ǂ	⍋ ∧ 74	⍋ △	⍋ ≙ 76	⍋ ⍋	⍋ ◇	⍋ ⟠

Write the Blurbo numbers.

88 _____ 81 _____ 45 _____ 33 _____

52 _____ 50 _____ 37 _____ 21 _____

FOCUS: Students use number sense to explore an alternate system for writing numbers.

Name ____

Team Spirit

Read the clues. Then write a number from the box on each shirt. Use each number only once.

23	98	53	44

1.

My number has fewer than 5 tens.

2. My number has more ones than tens.

3.

My number has 3 ones.

4. My number is greater than 50.

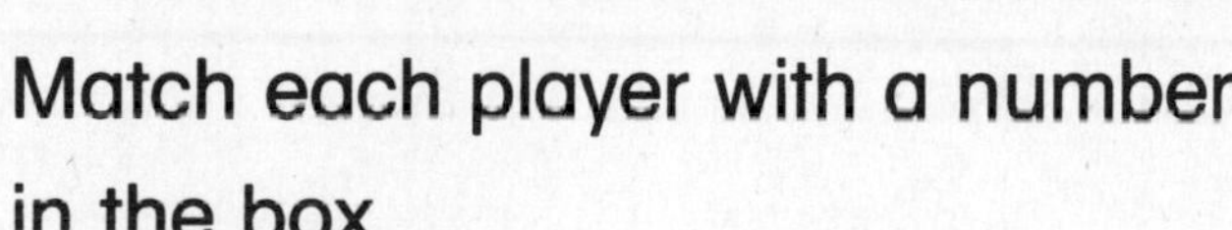

Match each player with a number in the box.

40	62	38	52

5.
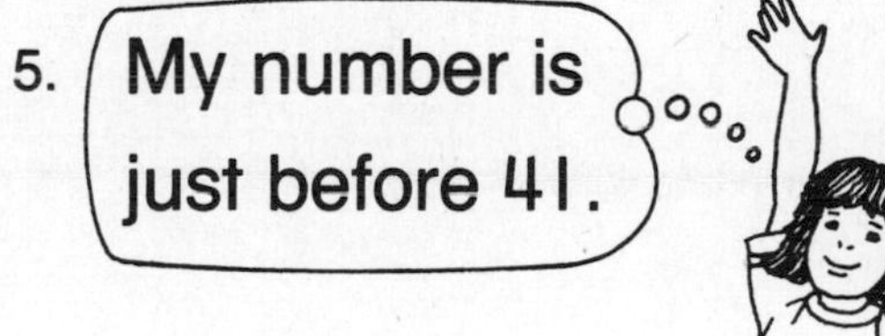
My number is just before 41.

6. My number is not between 61 and 63.

7.
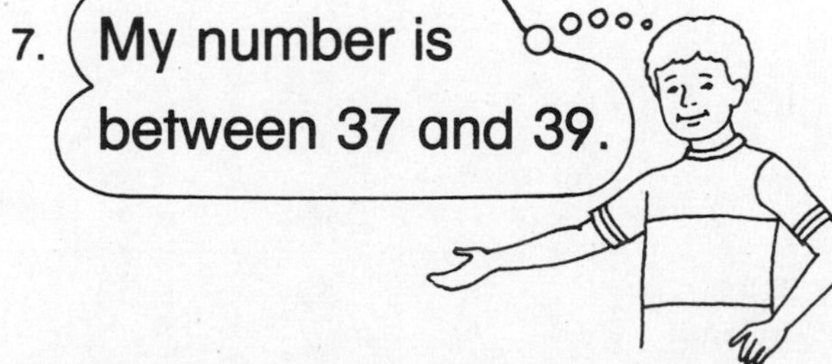
My number is between 37 and 39.

8. One number is mine.

> **FOCUS:** Students use deductive reasoning to solve logic problems.

Name ______________________________ **Relationships**

Use with text pages 109–110.

What's Missing?

Look for patterns in the chart. Then complete the sentences. Add numbers to the chart to help you.

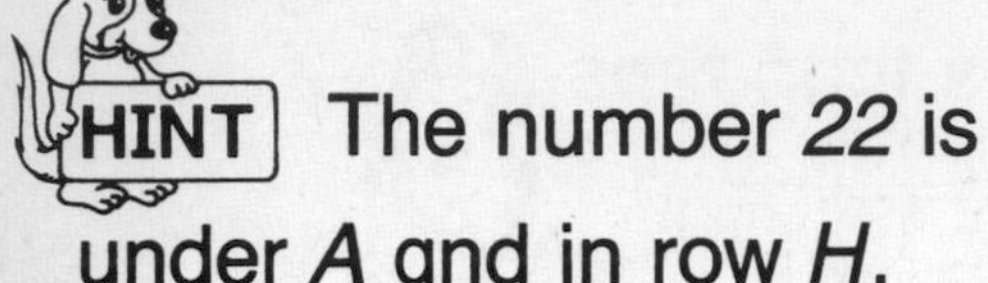

The number *22* is under *A* and in row *H*.

	A ↓	B ↓	C ↓	D ↓	E ↓
F →	2	4	6	8	10
G →	12	14	16	18	20
H →	22	24	26	28	30
I →	32	34	36	38	40
J →					
K →					

1. The numbers under D skip count by _____ .
2. The numbers in row H skip count by _____.
3. You will find 60 under letter _____ .
4. You will find 72 under letter _____ .
5. You will find 44 in row _____ .
6. You will find 52 in row _____ .
7. You will find 50 under letter _____ .
8. You will find 56 under letter _____ .

FOCUS: Students use counting skills to identify number patterns.

Name ______________________

Use with text pages 113–114.

How Many?

Skip count to find out how many are in each group. Then finish each sentence.

HINT You may need to count part of each group by ones.

1. 

There are ____ ★s.

I skip counted by ____.

2. 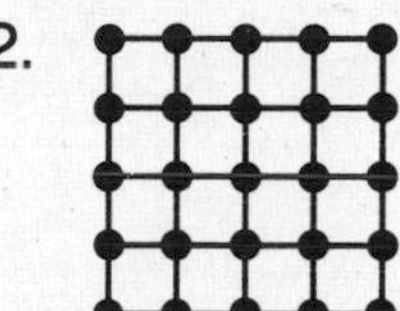

There are ____ •s.

I skip counted by ____.

3. 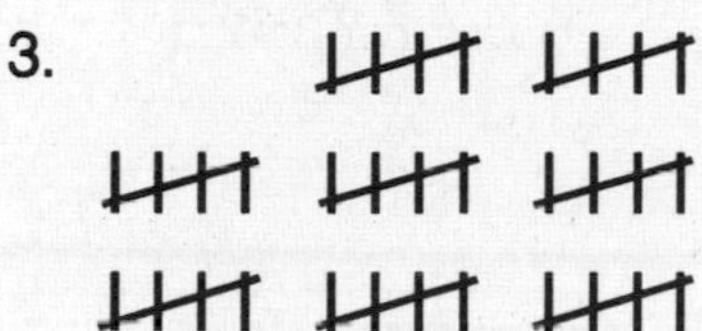

There are ____ ǀs.

I skip counted by ____.

4. 

There are ____ ǀs.

I skip counted by ____.

5. 

There are ____ ●s.

I skip counted by ____.

6. × × × ×
× × × ×
× × × ×
× × × ×

There are ____ ×s.

I skip counted by ____.

FOCUS: Students use skip-counting skills to count objects in an organized way.

Name ______________________________ **Decision Making/Problem Solving**

Use with text pages 115–116.

Shopping Trip

Ring the best buy in each row.

1.

GIANT-SIZE
ACME
RUBBER BANDS
Just 59¢
50 in a box

2.

3.

4.

FOCUS: Students use their knowledge of comparing numbers to make a purchasing decision.

Name ______________________________

Use with text pages 117–118.

Apartment for Rent

Read the clues. Cut out the pictures of the animals. Paste them on the floor in which they belong in the apartment house.

Check before you paste.

Clues

- Goat lives on the first floor.
- Duck lives on the floor just above the fourth floor.
- Cow does not live on the second or the sixth floor.
- Dog lives on the third floor.
- Cat lives on a higher floor than Horse does.

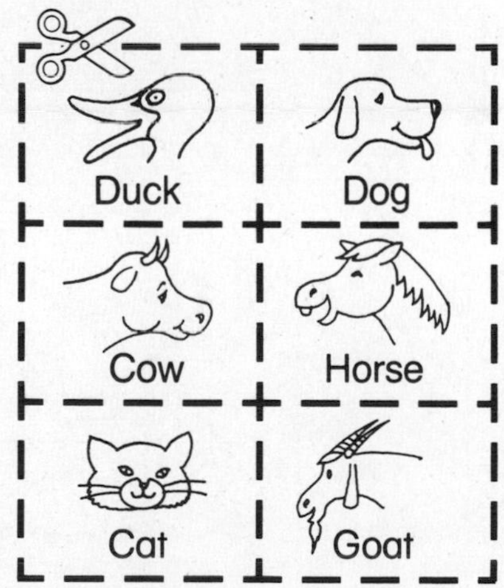

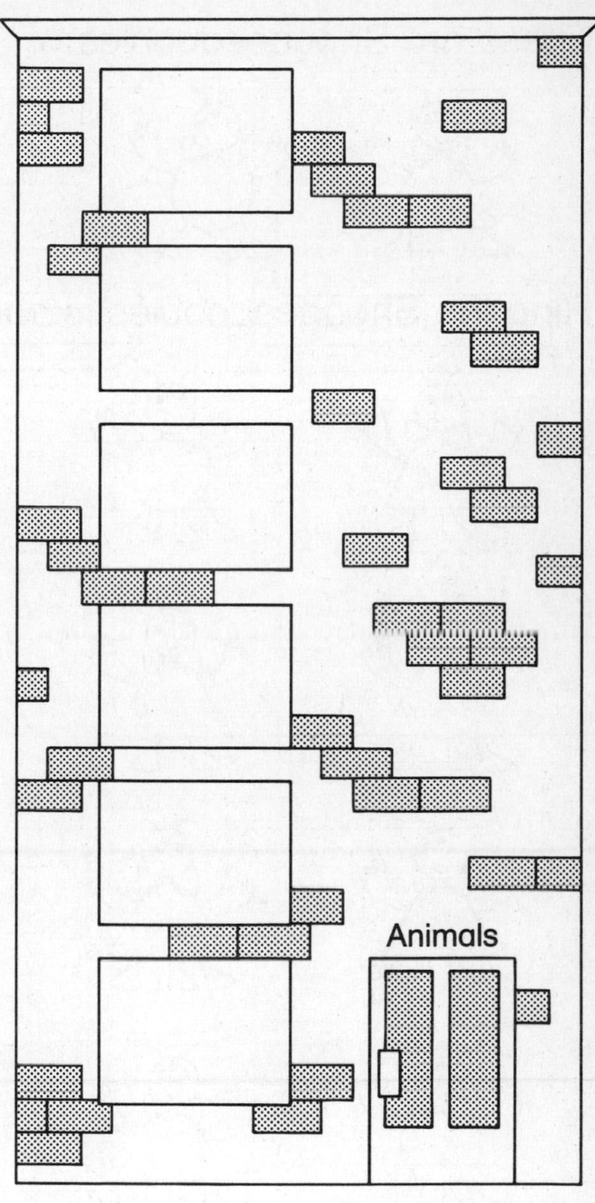

FOCUS: Students use their knowledge of ordinal numbers and deductive reasoning to solve a logic puzzle.

Name ______________________________ **Attributes**

Use with text pages 129–130.

Shoobeedoobie

These are Shoobeedoobies.

These are *not* Shoobeedoobies.

Ring the Shoobeedoobies in each group.

1.

2.

3.

4.

Share

Tell how you found the Shoobeedoobies.

FOCUS: Students compare attributes to determine whether figures belong in a group.

Name ____________________

Use with text pages 131–132.

Different Places

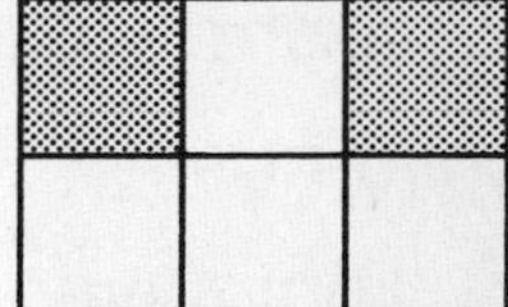

Look at the picture with 6 blocks. Two are shaded and four are white. In how many different places on the grid can you put the two shaded blocks? Color two squares in each grid to find out.

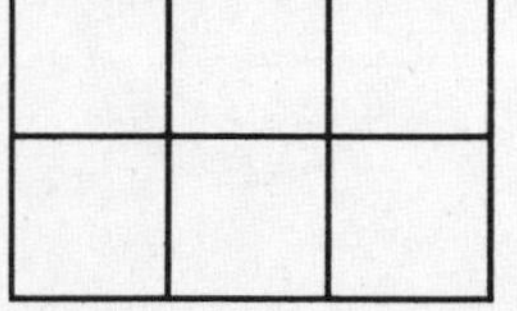
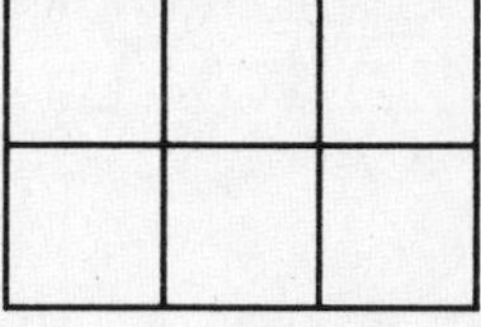
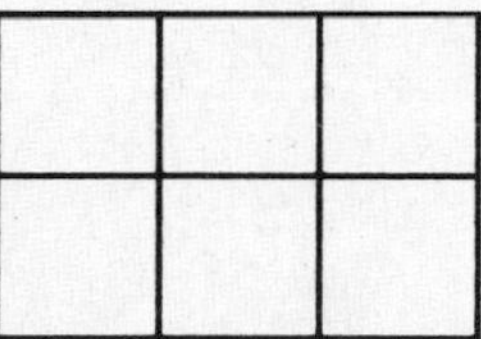
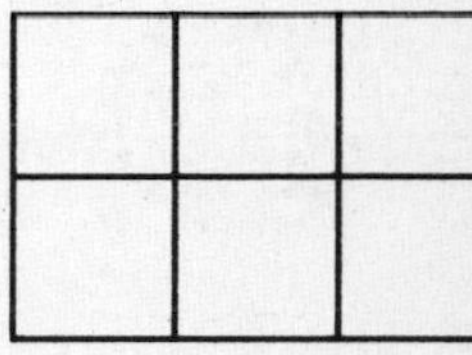
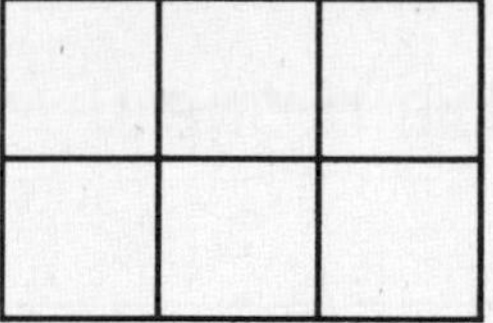
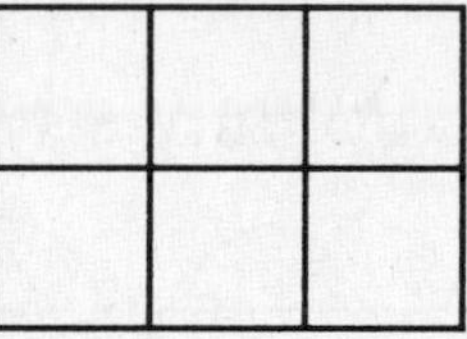
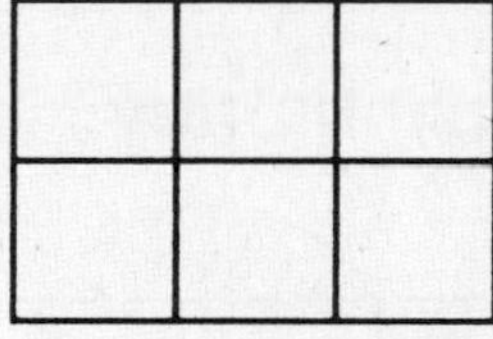
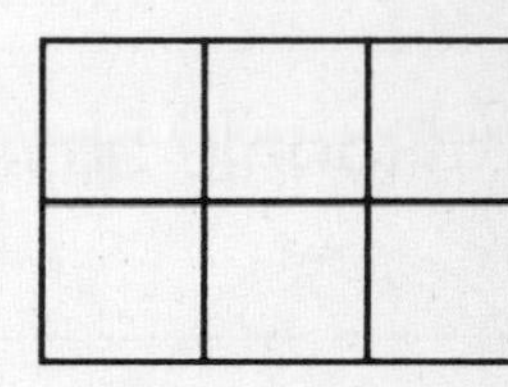
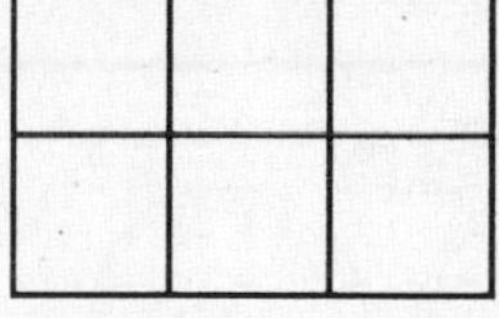
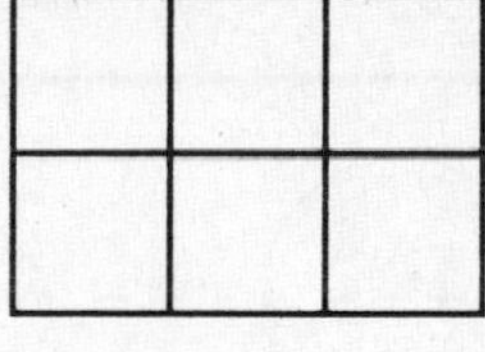
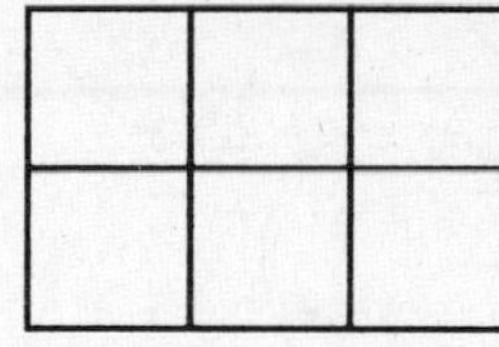
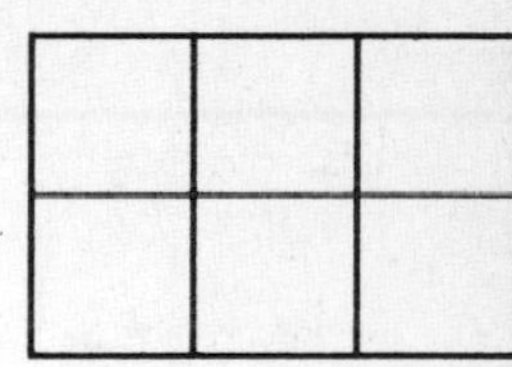
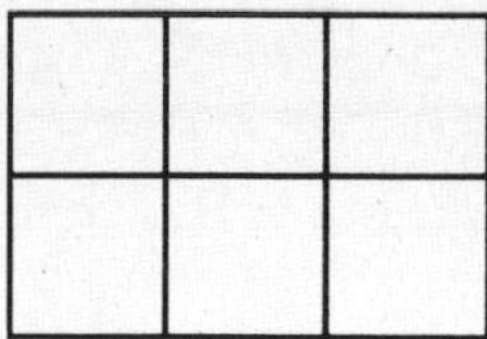
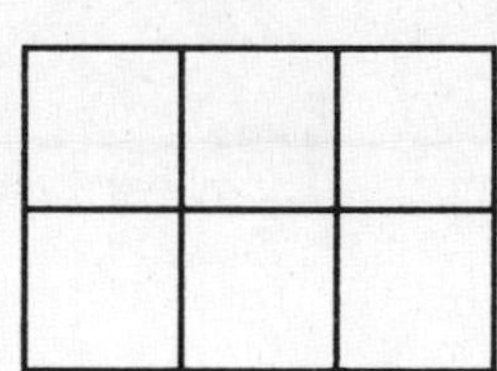
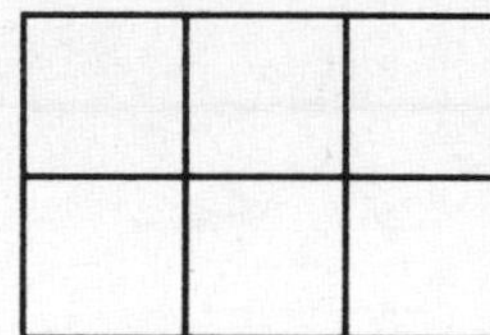

How many different ways did you find? _____

FOCUS: Students use mental imagery to create pattern variations.

Name ______________________________ **Problem Solving**

Use with text pages 135–136.

Save Up

Write the value of the coins that each child has.

1. Toni saved this money.

Toni has _____ ¢.

2. Joanie saved this money.

Joanie has _____ ¢.

3. Ronnie saved this money.

Ronnie has _____ ¢.

4. Johnny saved this money.

Johnny has _____ ¢.

Share

How did you solve the problems?

Tell a classmate.

FOCUS: Students determine the values of groups of coins.

Name ______________________________ **Logic**

Use with text pages 139–140.

Money Mystery

Complete the table. Use the clues.

- Jane has two coins.
- Jane has more than 26¢ and less than 31¢.
- Robert has one quarter.
- Sue has one coin.
- Sue has more money than Robert.
- John has three coins.
- John has 3¢ less than Jane.

COINS EACH CHILD HAS						
Child						**Total Value**
Jane						¢
Robert						¢
Sue						¢
John						¢

FOCUS: Students use deductive reasoning to solve a logic puzzle.

Name ______________________________ **Visual Thinking**

Use with text pages 141–142.

Coin Puzzles

Ring the two pieces in each row that fit together.

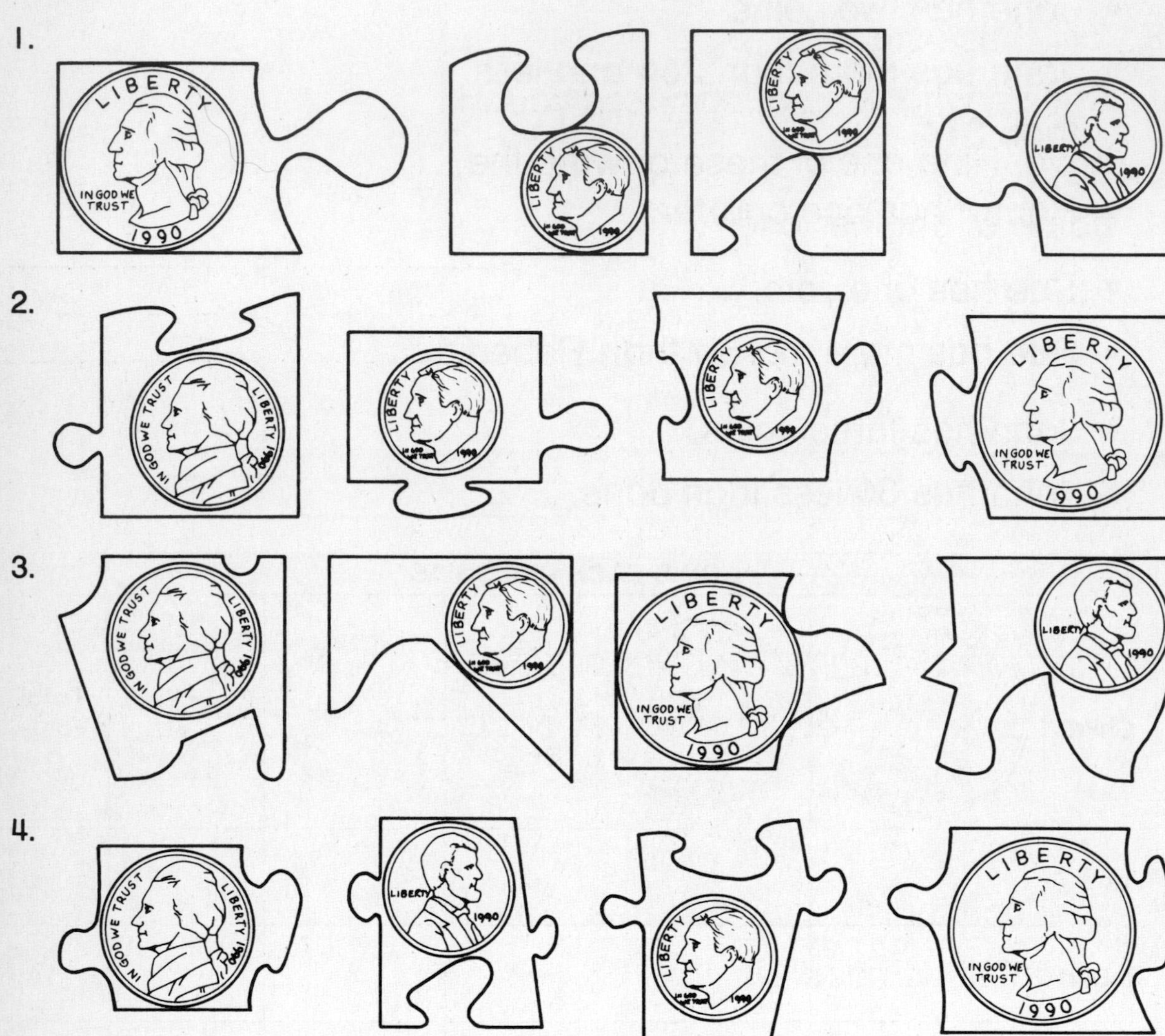

1.

2.

3.

4.

5. Look at the puzzle pieces with rings.

How much are the coins worth? _____ ¢

Compare your answer with a classmate's.

FOCUS: Students use visual sense to match pairs of puzzle pieces and use their knowledge of money to check their answers.

Name ________________________________ **Decision Making/Project**

Use with text pages 143–144.

Open for Business

Work with three other classmates. Make plans to run a store or other business. Follow these steps.

1. Decide what kind of business you will have. Ring one of these or write the name of another one.

   restaurant   fruit store   ______________

   toy store   book store

2. Think of a name for your store. Plan a sign for it. Draw it across the top of a large sheet of paper. Make it part of a poster.

3. Plan large posters to show what you would sell. Look in magazines or catalogs. Cut out 6 or more things that you would sell. Paste them on a large sheet of paper. You could also draw pictures. See the samples on page 38.

4. Make price tags. Cut out those on page 38 and write the correct prices on them. Paste the price tags next to each picture. Write prices from 1¢ to 50¢.

FOCUS: Students make decisions as they plan a play store and then make change as they make purchases.

Name ______________________ **Decision Making/Project**

Use with text pages 143–144.

Open for Business

Work with your group. Use punchout money and take turns as you shop at the store you pictured.

When you make change, remember to do this.

- Say the cost of the thing being bought.
- As you give back the coins, count up to the amount of money you were given.

Have fun as you shop. Change places with classmates in other groups and shop by using their posters.

___ ¢	___ ¢	___ ¢
___ ¢	___ ¢	___ ¢
___ ¢	___ ¢	___ ¢
___ ¢	___ ¢	___ ¢
___ ¢	___ ¢	___ ¢
___ ¢	___ ¢	___ ¢
___ ¢	___ ¢	___ ¢

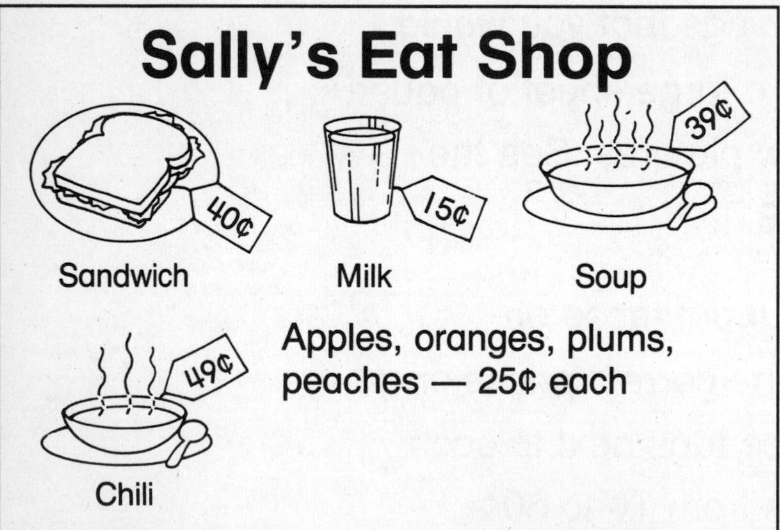

Sally's Eat Shop
40¢
Sandwich
15¢
Milk
39¢
Soup
49¢
Chili
Apples, oranges, plums, peaches — 25¢ each

FOCUS: Students make decisions as they plan a play store and then make change as they make purchases.

Name ____

Use with text pages 159–160.

Dot to Dot

Continue each pattern.

1.

2.

3.

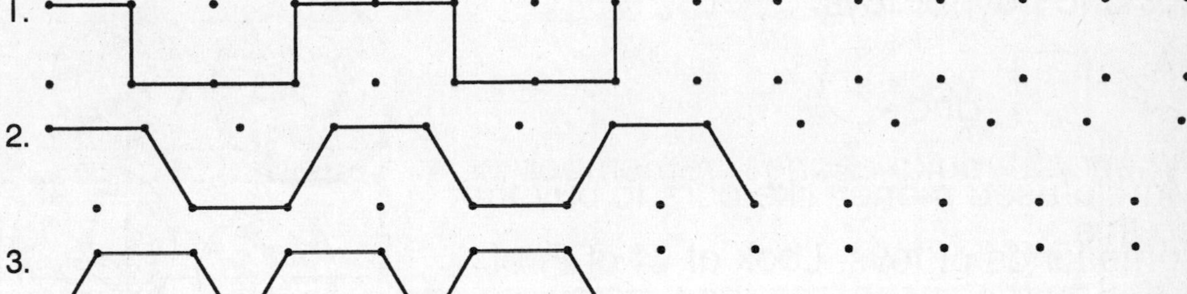

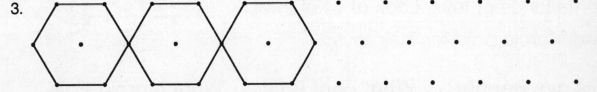

Create Your Own

Create your own pattern here.

Ask a classmate to continue it.

Copy your classmate's pattern here.

FOCUS: Students continue patterns on a dot grid and then create their own pattern for a classmate to continue.

Name ______________________________ **Logic**

Use with text pages 161–162.

Farstar Money

In Farstarland, Foof used these coins to pay for toys.

Marcia used money like ours to buy the same kinds of toys. Look at what Foof and Marcia paid for their toys.

Toys Bought	What Foof Paid	What Marcia Paid
•		 
• 	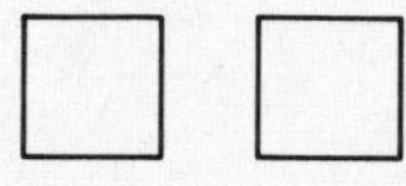	
• 		
• 		
• 		

Write the value of each Farstar coin in cents.

= ____ = ____ = ____

FOCUS: Students use number sense and logic to deduce the value of units in an invented monetary system.

Name ______________________________ **Visual Thinking**

Use with text pages 163–164.

The Creative Cat

Cut out the parts. Paste them in place to form the cat. Cut out the cat and paste it on a sheet of paper. Color it.

FOCUS: Students complete a tangram.

Name ______________________________ **Decision Making**

Use with text pages 167–168.

Happy Birthday

You want to send 3 birthday cards. You don't have supplies to make the cards. You do have 99¢. Ring what you would buy.

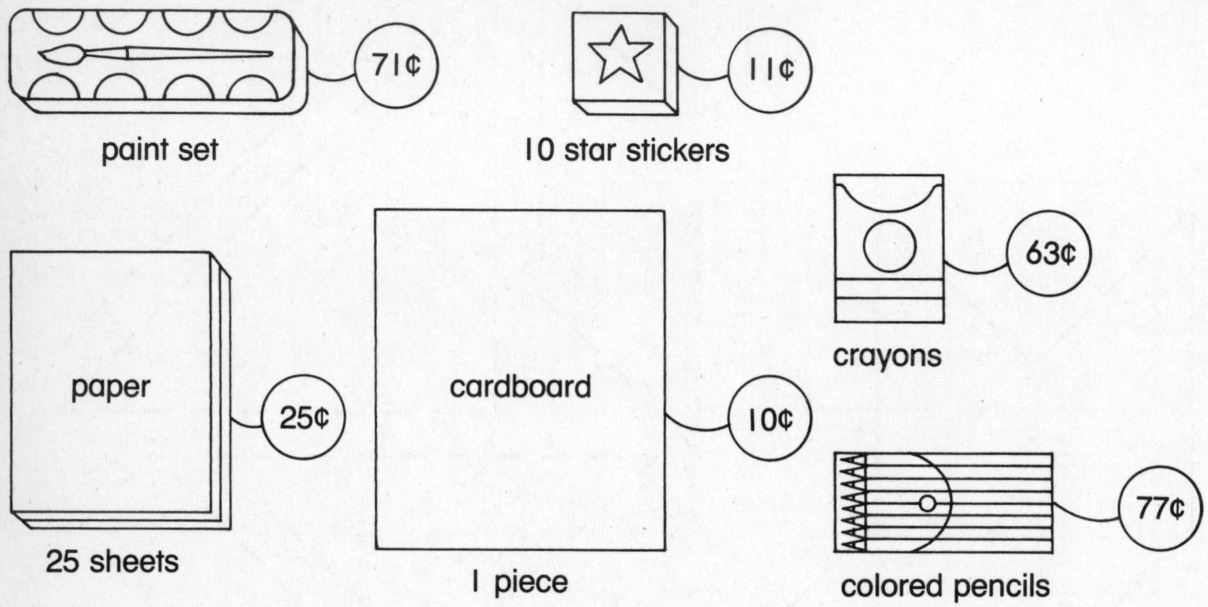

Write why you made the choices that you did.

____

____

____

____

FOCUS: Students make a purchasing decision based on monetary and consumer concerns.

Name ______________________________

Use with text pages 169–170.

Picture This

Look at the grid at the right.
Copy each shape in the
correct box on the grid.

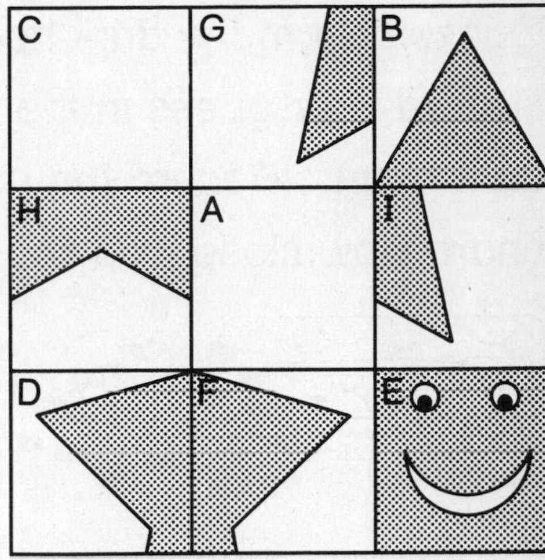

A	B	C
D	E	F
G	H	I

Write what you see.

I see a ______________________________ .

FOCUS: Students use visual thinking to copy shapes.

Too Many Beans

Guess how many dark beans are shown. Record your guess in the table. Count the dark beans. Record the number in the chart. How close was your guess? Explain.

Now do the same with the light beans. Then find the number of beans in all. How could you make the counting easier?

____

____

	Dark Beans	Light Beans	Total Beans
Your guess			
Your count			

Create Your Own

Draw some dark beans and light beans on the back of this page. Ask a classmate to guess how many there are.

FOCUS: Students use estimation skills to make a reasonable guess and use organized counting to find the total number.

Name ________________________________

Tally the Things

One tally mark looks like I.
Five tally marks look like ~~IIII~~.

Work with a group of 4 other children. Guess how many of each object your group has. You must be able to see the objects on the person or in the room. Then make tally marks to show how many. Next, write how many in all.

1. **Buttons**

   Guess: ____ Tally: [ ] Total: ____

2. **Pencils**

   Guess: ____ Tally: [ ] Total: ____

3. **Shoelace Holes**

   Guess: ____ Tally: [ ] Total: ____

4. **Red and Blue Crayons**

   Guess: ____ Tally: [ ] Total: ____

Share

Compare your totals with those of other groups.

FOCUS: Students use number sense to estimate and tally objects.

Name ____________________ **Logic**

Use with text pages 193–194.

Number Detective

Solve these math mysteries. Write the mystery number.

HINT When we write numbers, we use the digits 0, 1, 2, 3, 4, 5, 6, 7, 8, and 9. The number 94 has two digits, 9 and 4.

1. I am greater than 30.
   I am less than 40.
   One of my digits is 5.

   I am ____________________.

2. I am greater than 20.
   I am less than 34.
   The sum of my digits is 8.

   I am ____________________.

3. I am either 92, 27, or 78.
   The sum of my digits is less than 10.

   I am ____________________.

4. I am less than 79.
   I am greater than 61.
   One of my digits is 0.

   I am ____________________.

5. I am greater than 49.
   I am less than 60.
   Both of my digits are the same.

   I am ____________________.

6. I am either 20, 16, or 52.
   If you start at 0 and skip count by 5's, you will reach me.

   I am ____________________.

FOCUS: Students use deductive reasoning to solve number riddles.

Name ________________ **Problem Solving**

Use with text pages 195–196.

Number Please!

Replace each shape in a problem. Use the numbers in the box. Use each number only once. Then write the answer. The answers are not in the box.

12	14	35
17	8	28
7	46	

1. Lisa has △ model cars. Her sister has ⬡ cars. How many more cars does Lisa have than her sister?

   △ = ____

   ⬡ = ____

   Answer: ____ cars

2. Meg had [shape] marbles. Ann gave her [shape] marbles. How many marbles does Meg have now?

   [shape] = ____

   [shape] = ____

   Answer: ____ marbles

3. Tim has □ baseball cards. Ed has ⇦ baseball cards. How many more baseball cards does Tim have than Ed?

   □ = ____

   ⇦ = ____

   Answer: ____ cards

4. Mike picked up ✳ jacks. Billy picked up ☾ jacks. How many jacks did Mike and Billy pick up?

   ✳ = ____

   ☾ = ____

   Answer: ____ jacks

FOCUS: Students choose sensible numbers from a box to complete word problems involving addition and subtraction.

Name ______________________________ **Decision Making**

Use with text pages 201–202.

Soup Is On

What would you like for lunch? You have 85¢. Ring three or more things that you could buy.

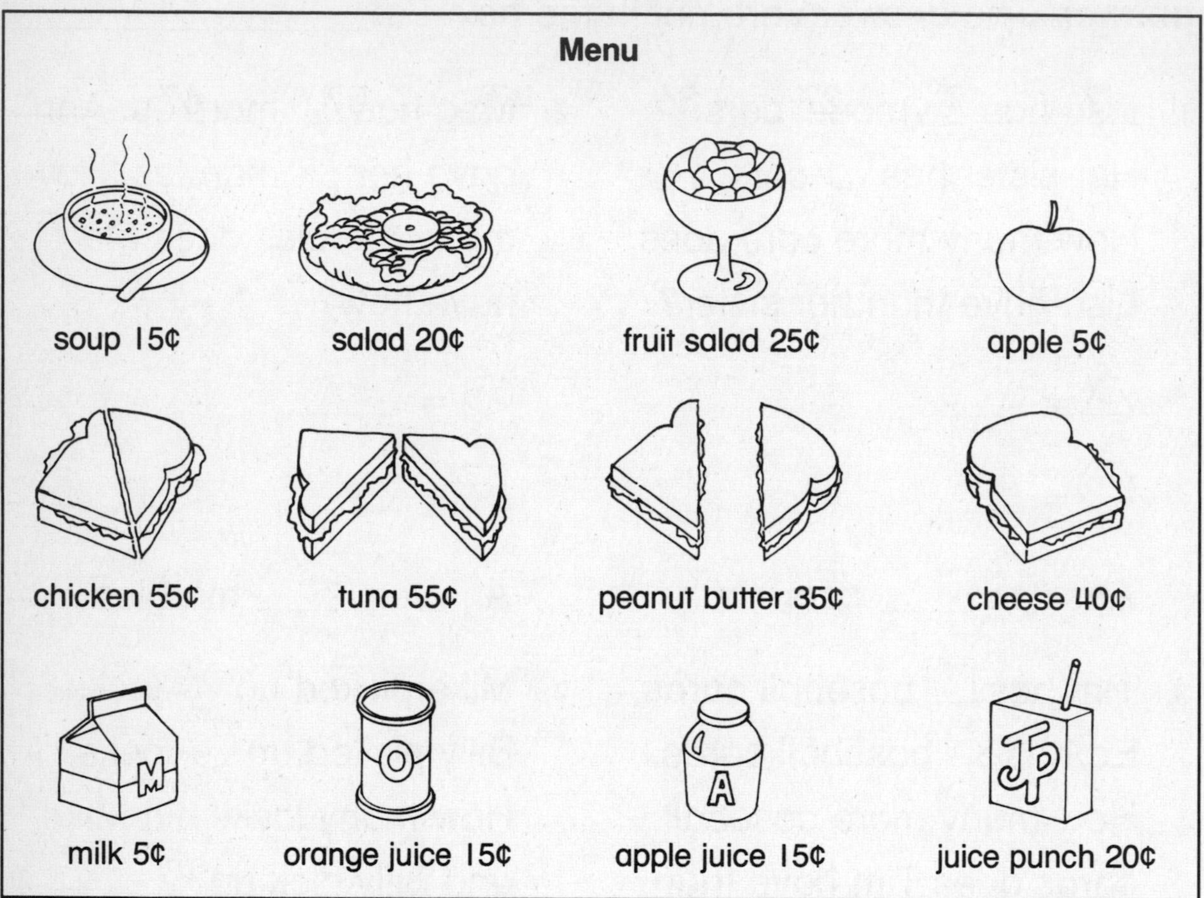

Complete the sentences.

I spent _____¢.

I have _____¢ change.

FOCUS: Students use personal preference and price to make a purchasing decision.

Name ____________________ **Attributes**

Use with text pages 203–204.

Sorry, Wrong Number!

Try to find a pattern in each row. One number does not fit the pattern. Cross it out. Write on the line the number that fits the pattern.

1.	7	17	27	36	47	57	67	____
2.	11	22	33	44	54	66	77	____
3.	5	18	29	41	53	65	77	____
4.	88	76	65	54	43	32	21	____
5.	3	6	9	12	15	18	23	____
6.	86	80	74	69	62	56	50	____
7.	94	93	91	88	84	78	73	____
8.	77	74	70	68	65	62	59	____
9.	20	40	60	50	100	120	140	____
10.	90	80	70	60	55	40	30	____
11.	13	27	39	52	65	78	91	____
12.	42	40	38	36	24	32	30	____

FOCUS: Students identify the number that does not belong in a series of numbers.

Name ______________________________ **Decision Making/Project**

Use with text pages 207–208.

Making Beads

Here are some directions for making a clay bead necklace. Number each group to show the order.

Making the Beads (Steps 1 – 4)

_____ Make a hole in each bead for the string.

_____ Form some clay to make beads.

_____ Make a design on each bead with a toothpick.

_____ Let the beads harden.

Finishing the Necklace (Steps 5 – 8)

_____ Let the paint dry.

_____ Tie a knot in the string.

_____ String the beads.

_____ Paint each bead.

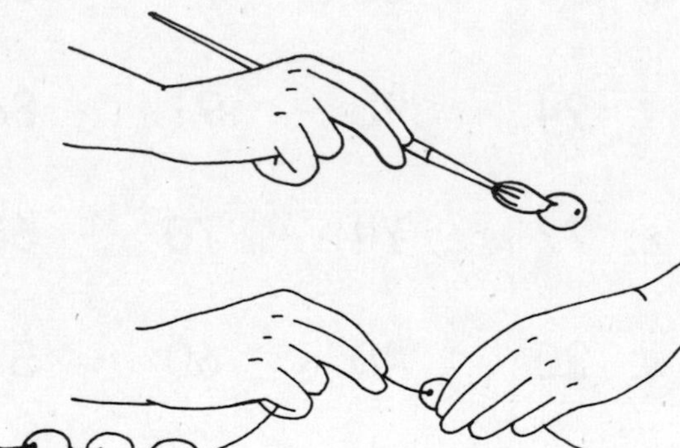

Share

Compare your list of steps with those of a classmate. Will you make any changes? Explain.

FOCUS: Students order steps required for making a bead necklace from clay.

Beads

Part Two: Plan Ahead

Make plans for one necklace.

1. Draw the size bead that you want to make.

2. Write how many beads you want to make. __________

3. Weigh the amount of clay that you think you will need. Write its weight.

   ____

4. Cut a piece of string to fit around your neck. Measure the string. __________

Share

Share your plans with your classmates. Are any of your amounts too great? Are any too little? Make changes if you need to. Then make your necklace with your partner.

FOCUS: Students make plans for making a necklace with clay beads.

Name ______________________________ **Logic**

Use with text pages 217–218.

Tick-Tock

Read the clues. Ring the watch or clock that fits all three clues.

HINT Cross out a picture after you read each clue.

- It does not have a wristband.
- It does not have a handle.
- It shows a time between 1:00 and 5:00.

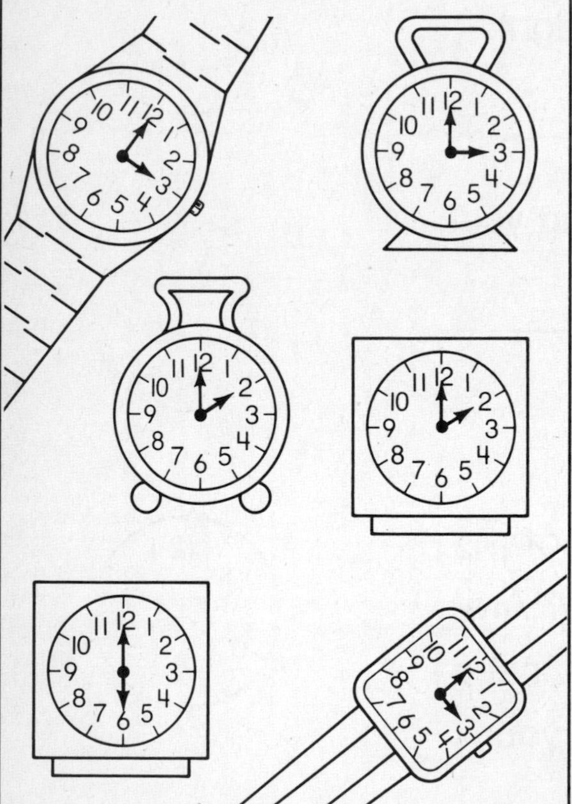

- It has an hour and a minute hand.
- It does not have stripes.
- It shows the same time as another watch or clock.

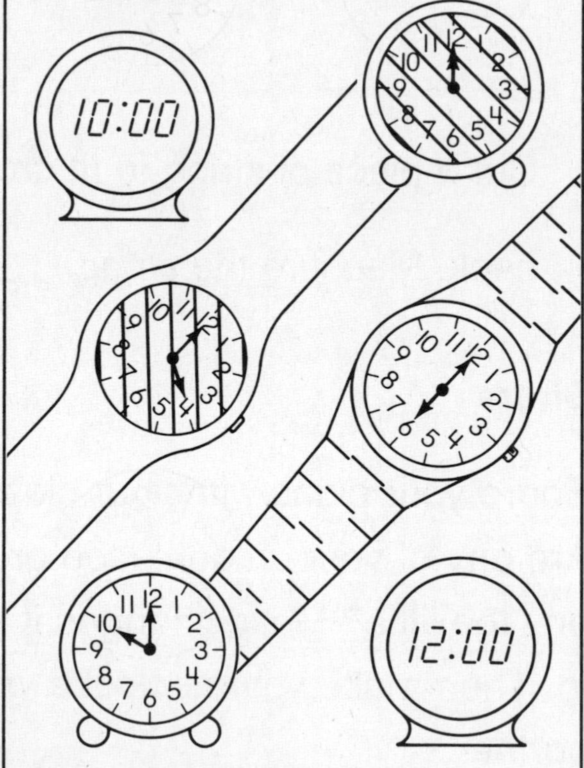

FOCUS: Students use deductive reasoning and their knowledge of time to solve logic problems.

Name ______________________________

Patterns in Schedules

Each schedule for a class follows a pattern. Draw hands on the last clock to continue the pattern.

Schedules

1. Art classes

2. Dance classes

   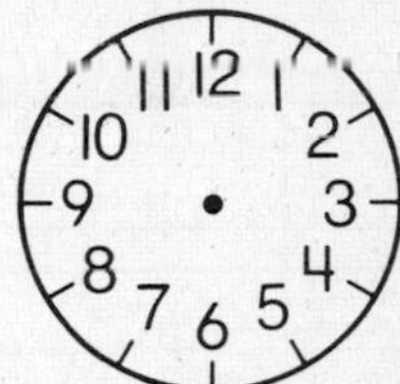

3. Tumbling classes

4. Music classes

FOCUS: Students use their knowledge of telling time to the hour to continue patterns shown on clock faces.

Name ______________________ **Number Sense**

Use with text pages 221–222.

Make a Ten

Make the six cards shown here. Place them in a bag. Remove a card and write the number on the chart. Put the card back in the bag. Take 5 turns. If you score 10 or more, you win the game. See how many games you can win.

1	1	1
3	2	5

Game 1	
Turn	**Score**
1	
2	
3	
4	
5	
Total	

Game 2	
Turn	**Score**
1	
2	
3	
4	
5	
Total	

Game 3	
Turn	**Score**
1	
2	
3	
4	
5	
Total	

Share

I won ____ out of 3 games.

Is it easier to win or to lose? ________

Play 3 more games. Keep score on the back of this paper. Play with a partner. Which number did you pull most often? ____

FOCUS: Students use number sense to predict the outcome of a set of events.

Name ____ **Logic**

Use with text pages 225–226.

Party Time

What time did each child come to the party? Read the clues. Draw the clock hands to show the arrival times.

Arrival Times		
3:10	3:15	3:20
3:40	3:55	4:05

HINT Cross out each arrival time after you show it on a clock.

Clues

- Chris came first.
- When Kenny came, the minute hand was on 4.
- When Jesse came, the minute hand and the hour hand were very close to each other.
- When Merle came, the minute hand was on 1.
- Mario came 10 minutes before Merle.
- Karla came 20 minutes after Kenny did.

Kenny

Merle

Chris

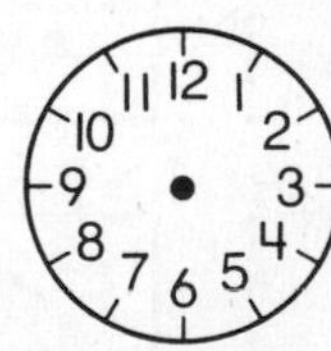

Jesse

Mario

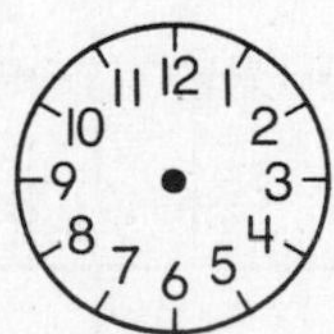

Karla

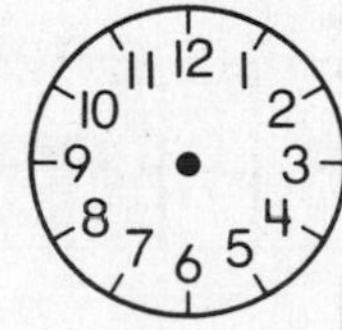

FOCUS: Students use their knowledge of time and deductive reasoning to solve a logic puzzle.

In What Order?

Jason has these things to do this afternoon. Show the order in which he should do them. Number them from 1 to 5.

_____ Sign up for dodgeball at the playground between 1:30 and 3:30.

_____ Watch boat race at pond between 2:30 and 3:30.

_____ Pick up bike at Fix-It Shop before 5:00.

_____ Jeff is going to camp tonight. See him before 4:30.

_____ Buy milk for dinner. The Corner Store closes at 6:00.

Now draw a line on the map to show his path. Number the stops.

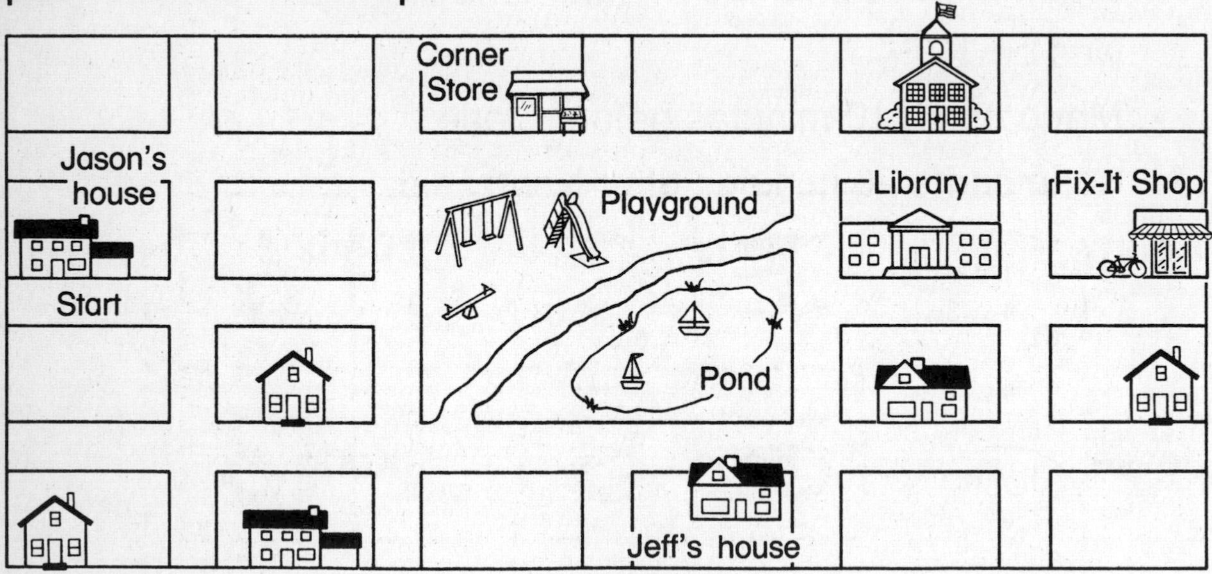

FOCUS: Students order a list of tasks with time constraints and then mark a map to show that order.

Name ____________________

Use with text pages 229–230.

Days of the Month

Make a calendar for this month.
Paste the letters and numbers in correct order on a piece of paper.
Decorate your calendar.
The picture shows you how to start.

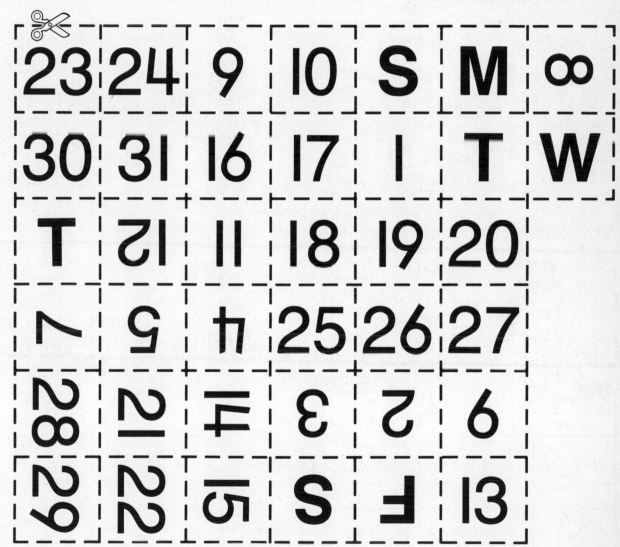

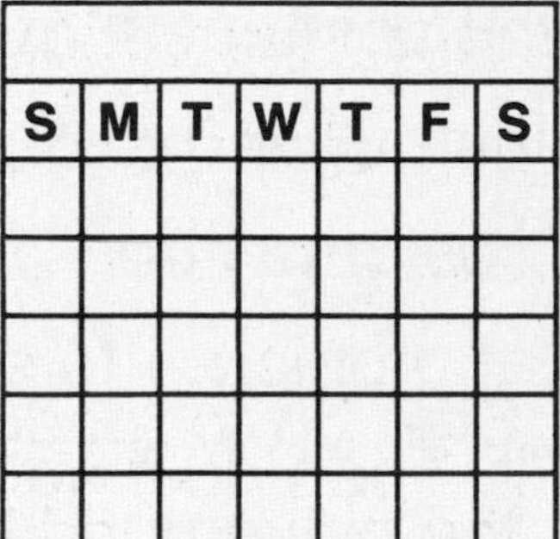

23	24	9	10	S	M	8
30	31	16	17	1	T	W
T	12	11	18	19	20	
7	5	4	25	26	27	
28	21	14	3	2	6	
29	22	15	S	F	13	

FOCUS: Students use visual thinking as they make a calendar.

Name ____________________

Costume Party

Pick the costume that you like the most. Give 0 to 6 points for each costume part. Then add. Look at problem 1 to see how to do it. Then do it again.

Points

6 means you like it a lot.
3 means you like it somewhat.
0 means you do not like it.

Ring the costume with the most points.

Share

Talk with classmates. Tell why you chose the winner that you did.

FOCUS: Students use a rating system to make a decision.

Name ____________________

Favorite Games

Read the clues. Complete the pictograph.
Cut and paste to do it.

Clues

- Three children like to play catch.
- Two more children like swimming more than they like to play catch.
- The same number of children like to jump rope and play dodge ball.
- The fewest number of children like hopscotch.

Games Liked by Children

Jump Rope	
Hopscotch	
Basketball	
Dodge Ball	
Swimming	
Catch	

FOCUS: Students use deductive reasoning to complete a pictograph.

Name ____________________ **Number Sense**

Use with text pages 237–238.

Pets on Parade

Read about each class's pets. Then match the graph to the facts it tells about. Write the letter of the graph. Then write a title for the graph.

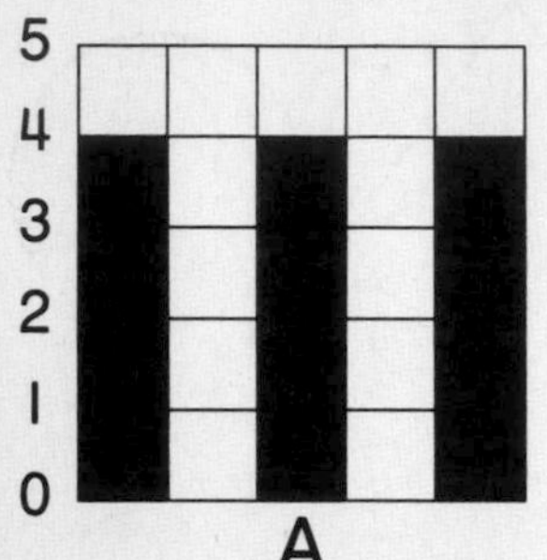

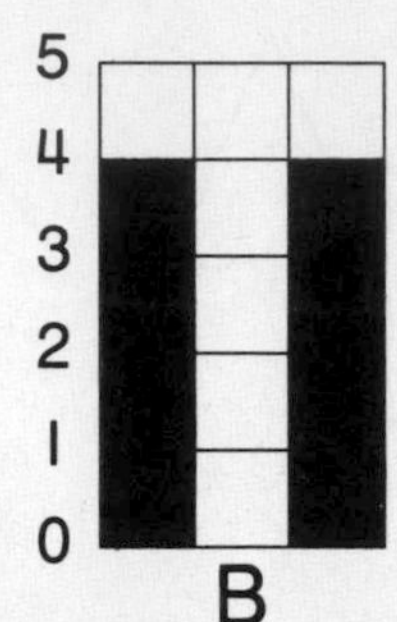

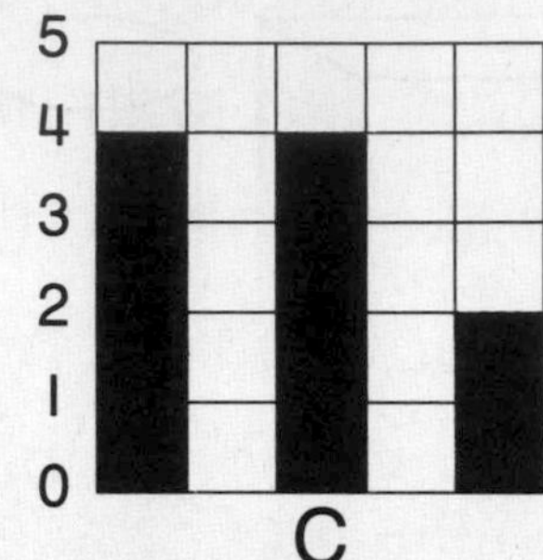

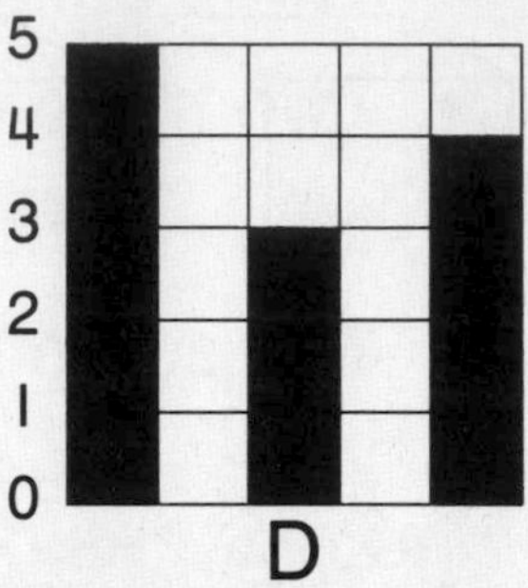

1. Five children in Mr. Lee's class have fish. Three have dogs. Four have turtles.

   ____

   ____

2. In Ms. Kim's class, the same number of children have dogs, cats, and turtles.

   ____

   ____

3. In Ms. Sol's class, four children have cats and four have dogs. No one has fish.

   ____

   ____

4. In Mr. Tam's class, two children have gerbils. Four have dogs. Four have cats.

   ____

   ____

FOCUS: Students use number sense to select the graph that fits a set of data.

Name ________________________________ **Visual Thinking**

Use with text pages 249–250.

Shapes Around Us

Many objects around us look like these shapes. We can see these shapes in buildings. We see them in many things that we have in our homes and in schools.

Find some magazines with many pictures. Find pictures of objects that look something like the shapes. Sometimes an object will show two or more shapes. Cut out the pictures and sort them. Paste pictures that show one kind of shape on a large sheet of paper. Make a poster for each different shape. Make a title for each poster.

Share

Share your posters with all of your classmates. Did you choose pictures of the same objects?

FOCUS: Students use their visual sense to identify objects that have the shape of cubes, cones, cylinders, rectangular prisms, spheres, and pyramids.

Have available old magazines that contain many pictures, large poster paper, paste, and markers.

Name ______________________________ **Visual Thinking**

Use with text pages 251–252.

Construction Workers

Write how many straws and clay balls you will need to build each figure. Then build one of the figures.

Note: You will need nonhardening clay and plastic drinking straws. If you wish, cut straws in half.

1. _____ straws

   _____ clay balls

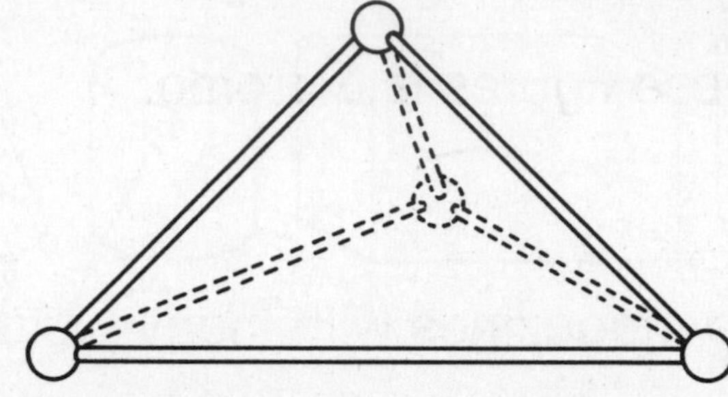

2. _____ straws

   _____ clay balls

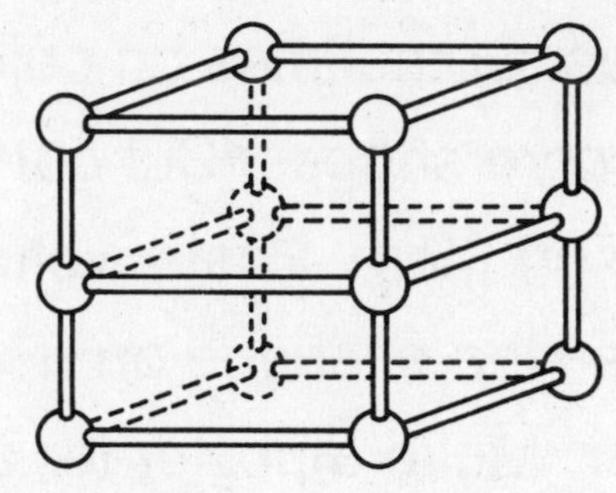

3. _____ straws

   _____ clay balls

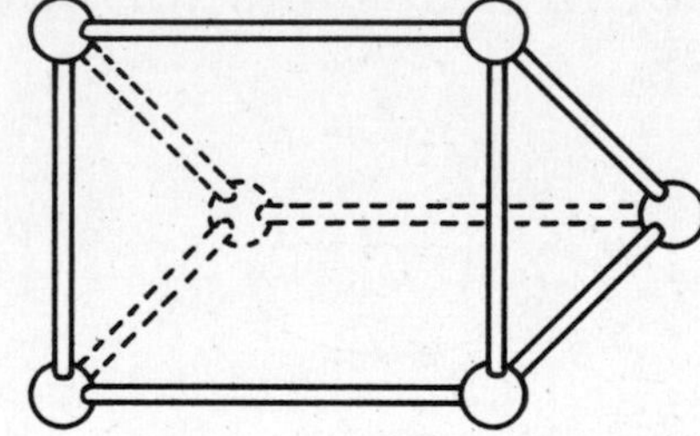

Create Your Own

Construct your own figure. Use 8 clay balls and 12 straws.

FOCUS: Students use their knowledge of spatial relationships to reproduce geometric figures.

Name ____ **Relationships**

Use with text pages 253–254.

Clay Figures

Ketti makes clay figures.

Her favorite kind is a *dromo*.

Decide how all dromos are alike.

Each of these figures is a dromo.

 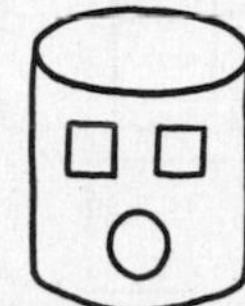 

None of these figures is a dromo.

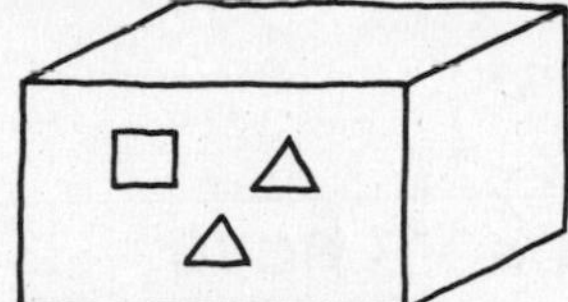  

Which of these figures are dromos? Ring each dromo.

1. 
2. 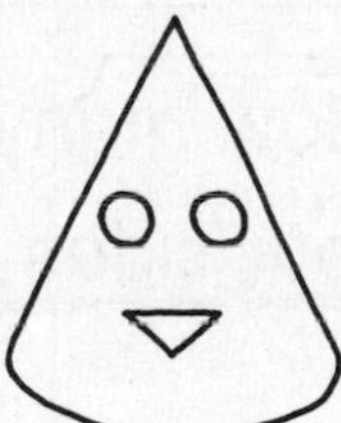
3. 
4. 

5. Choose a partner. Compare answers.
   Talk about what makes a figure a dromo.

   ____

   ____

FOCUS: Students analyze figures and identify why certain figures fit into a particular group.

Stick to It!

The graph shows how many different stickers Paula has. Use the graph to help you solve each problem. Write the letter A, B, C, or D to tell how how you solved it.

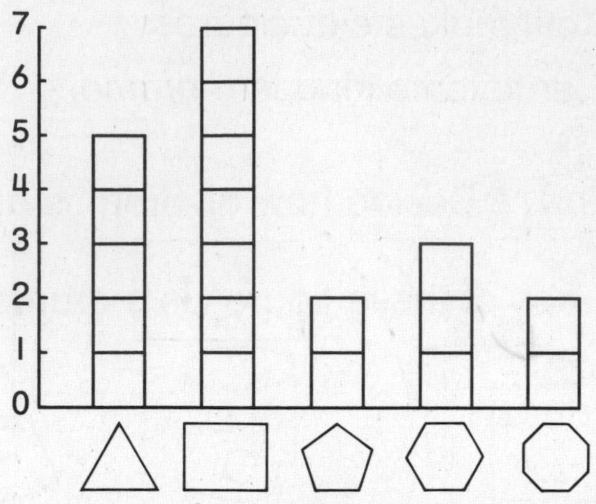

How I Solved the Problem

A. I counted.

B. I added.

C. I counted and added.

D. I read only the graph.

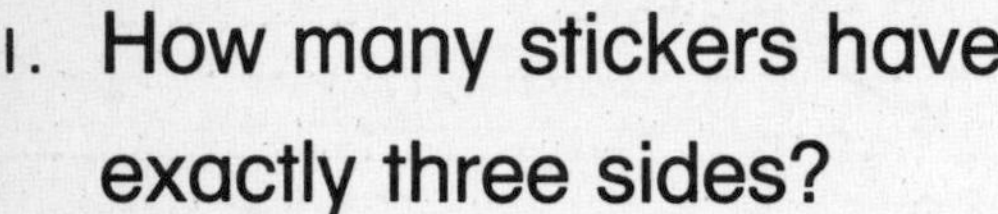

1. How many stickers have exactly three sides?

____

4. How many stickers have fewer than three sides?

____

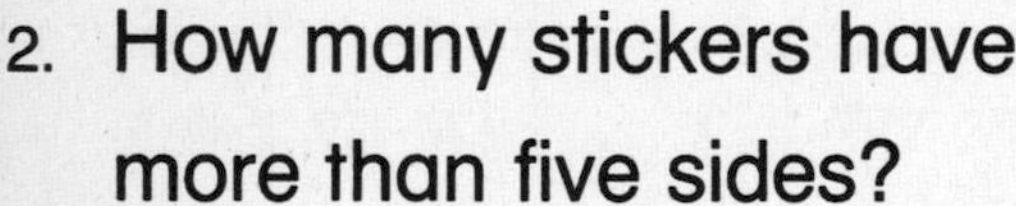

2. How many stickers have more than five sides?

____

5. How many stickers have four sides or more?

____

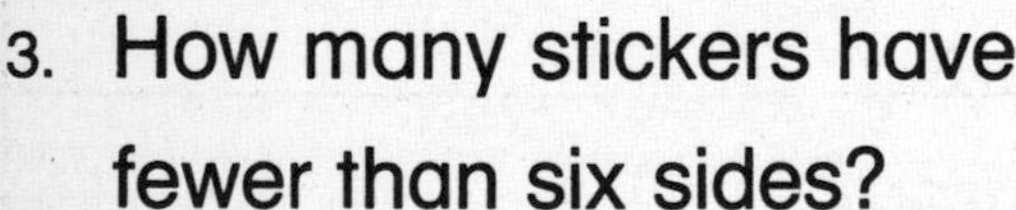

3. How many stickers have fewer than six sides?

____

6. How many stickers have more than eight sides?

____

7. Paula has __________ stickers altogether.

FOCUS: Students solve problems based on data given in a graph and identify the methods that they used.

Name ____________________ **Logic**

Use with text pages 265–266.

Sorting Flags

Complete the chart below.

Use tally marks and numbers.

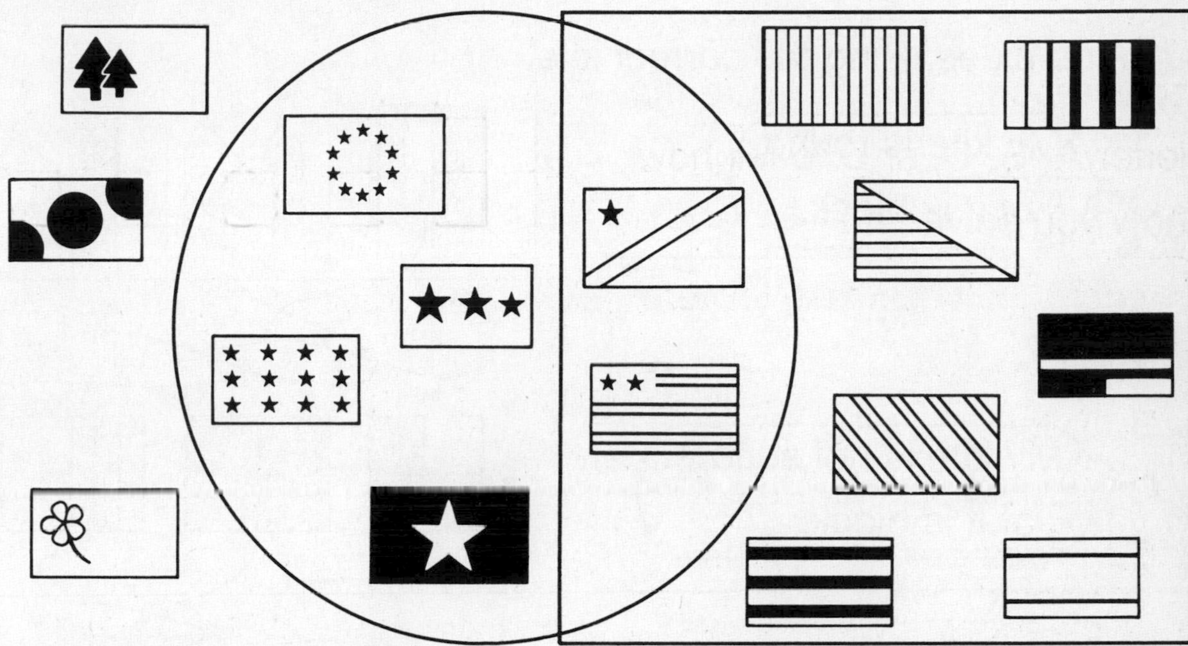

Places for Flags	Tally	Number
Flags in the circle		
Flags in the square		
Flags in both the circle and the square		
Flags not in the circle or the square		
Flags in all		

FOCUS: Students use logic to interpret a Venn diagram.

Fly a Kite

The kites are tangled up. Help the frogs find their kites.

Use the clues. Ring the correct kite.

1. My kite is round.
$\frac{2}{3}$ of it is black.

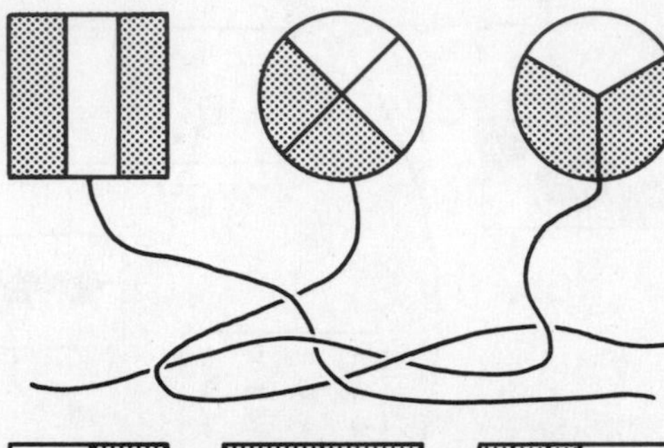

2. My kite is not square.
$\frac{3}{4}$ of it is black.

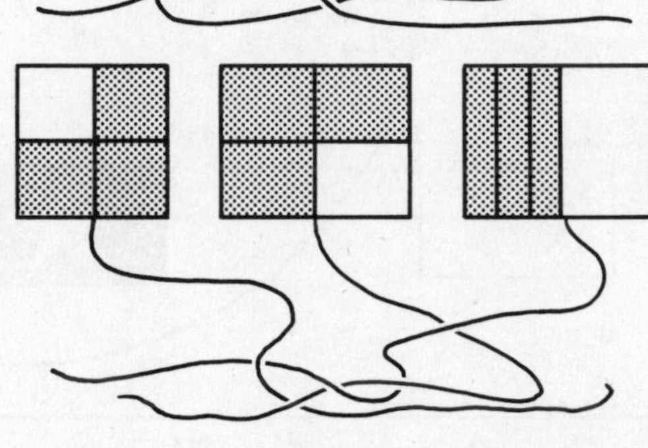

3. My kite is not a triangle.
The black part is not $\frac{1}{4}$ of it.

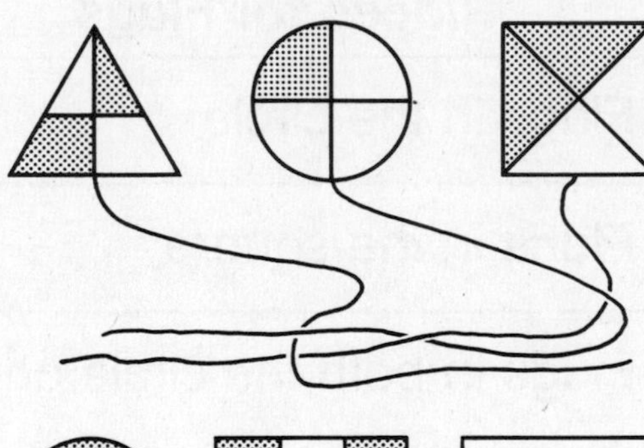

4. My kite is not square.
It is not round.
The black part is not $\frac{2}{3}$ of it.

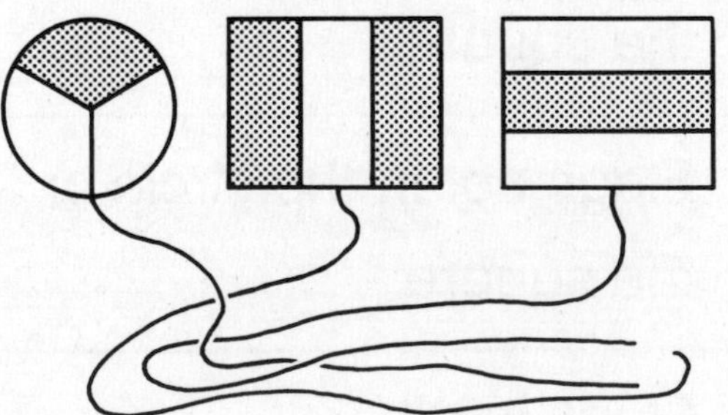

FOCUS: Students use deductive reasoning to identify the object described.

Name ______________________________

Use with text pages 269–270.

Rhyme Time

Each problem tells about a part of a group of things. Find each answer. Draw pictures or use counters to help you.

1. Rub-a-dub dub.
   16 birds in a tub.
   $\frac{1}{2}$ of them fly away.
   How many birds fly away?

   ____

2. Hickory dickory dock.
   12 mice on a clock.
   $\frac{1}{4}$ of them run away.
   How many mice run away?

   ____

3. Hey diddle diddle.
   12 ants on a fiddle.
   $\frac{1}{3}$ of them crawl off.
   How many ants crawl off?

   ____

4. Little Miss Tuppels
   had 14 puppets.
   $\frac{1}{2}$ of them were broken.
   How many puppets were broken?

   ____

Ring the best estimate for this problem.

5. Old King Nolls
   Made 36 rolls.
   $\frac{1}{2}$ of the rolls were sold.
   How many rolls are left?

   more than 10   less than 10

FOCUS: Students use manipulatives or drawings and number sense to solve problems involving parts of a group.

Name ____________________ **Visual Thinking**

Use with text pages 271–272.

Making Pizza Pies

Cut out the pieces of pie. Paste them on the circles to show whole pies.

For these pies, the parts of each pie must all be the same size.

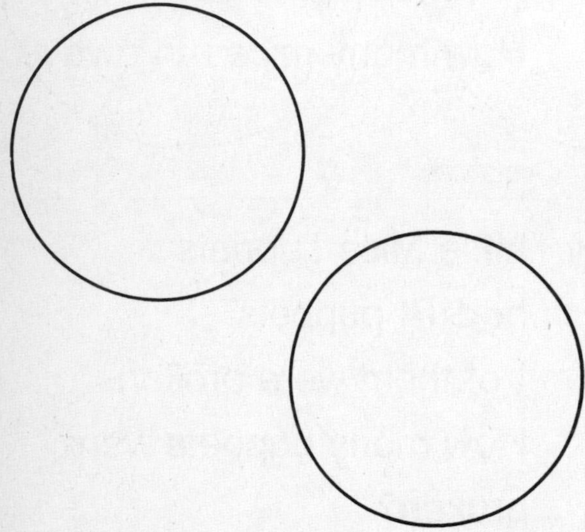

For this pie, some of the parts must be of a different shape and size. Be sure you make exactly one whole pie.

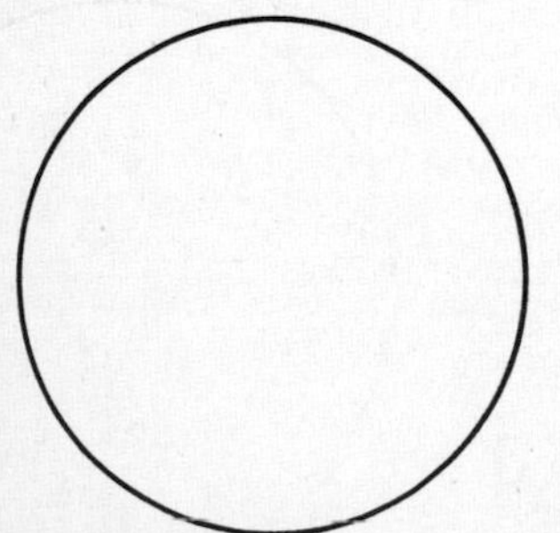

Pieces to Cut

Cut along the broken lines. You will not use all of the pieces.

FOCUS: Students use manipulatives to show that $\frac{2}{2} = 1$ and that one whole can be made with parts of the same size or with parts that are not all the same size.

Name ______________________________

Use with text pages 273–274.

Spin the Spinner

Color the part where the spinner would stop more times.

1.

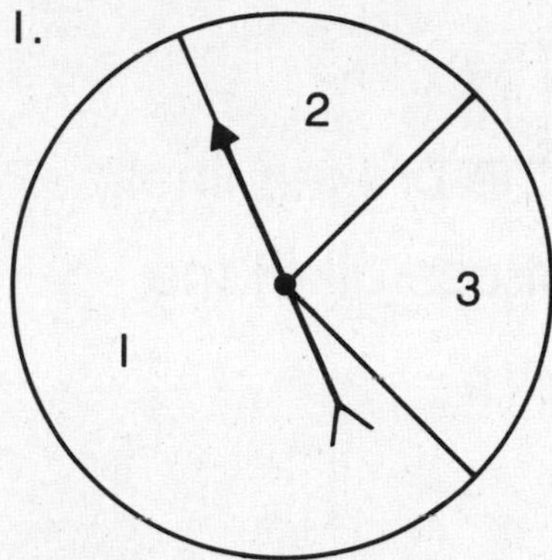

2.

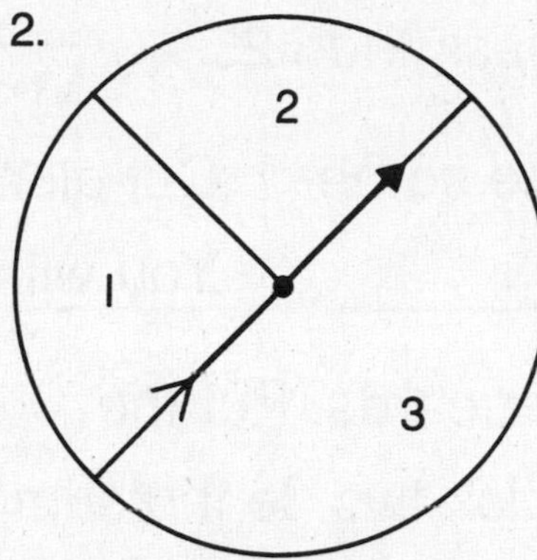

3.

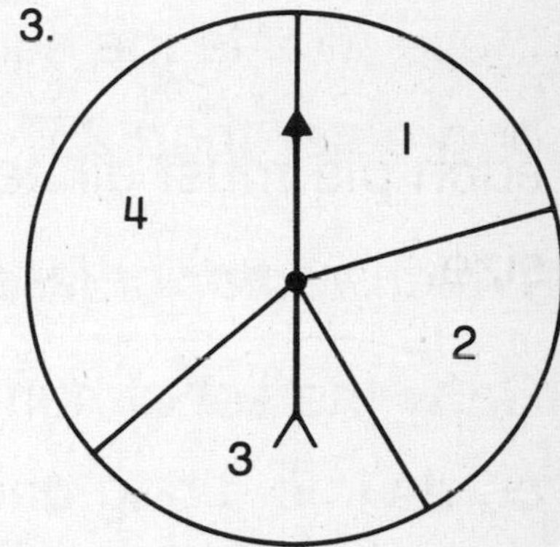

Color the part where the spinner would stop fewer times.

4.

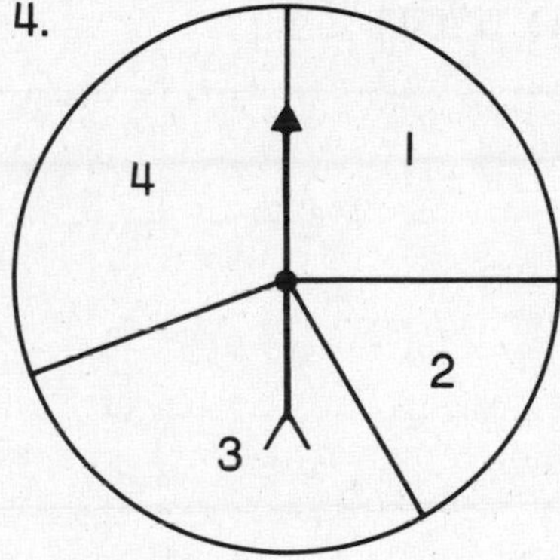

5.

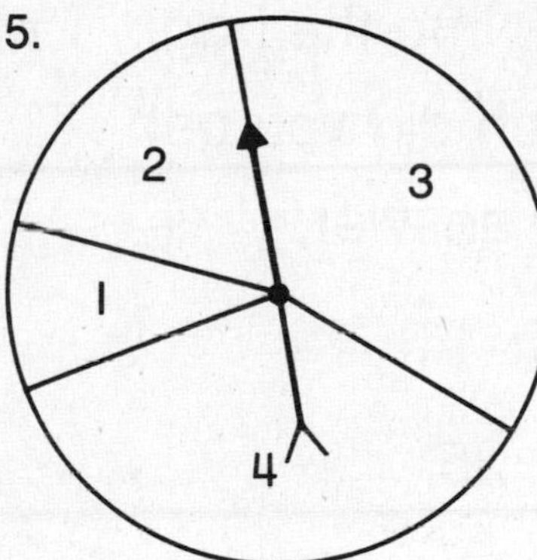

6.

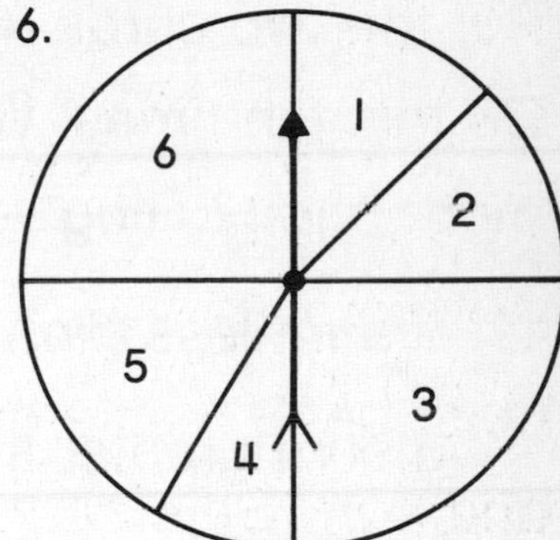

Create Your Own

Draw a spinner with two parts. Number the parts 1 and 2. Make the spinner so that it will stop more times on part 1.

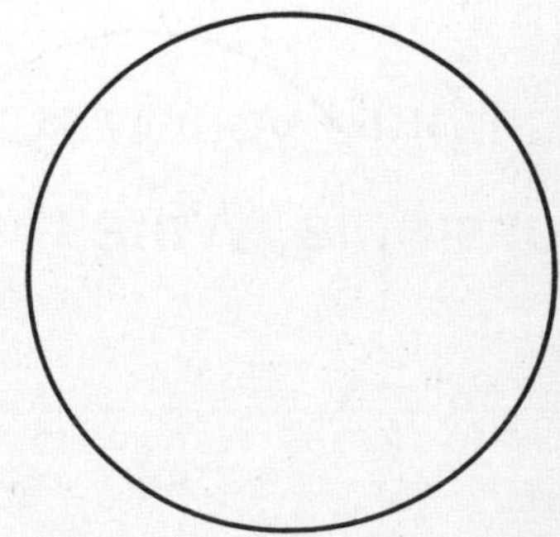

FOCUS: Students determine the probability of an event by marking a part of a circle.

Some Sums

Karen made these five number cards.

8	12	16	20	24

She put them in a bag and picked these two. Is the sum less than 25 or greater than 25?

12	16

Write *greater* or *less*. ________________

Copy the set of number cards. Put the cards into a bag and pick two. Is the sum less than 25 or greater than 25? Write a tally mark in the correct place on the chart. Pick two cards and add them. Put the two cards back into the bag. Do this ten times. Which did you get more often? Ring your answer.

Less than 25	
More than 25	

a sum less than 25

a sum greater than 25

Share

Compare your results with those of a classmate. Were they similar? Why?

____

____

FOCUS: Students use number sense to analyze a probability situation.

Name ____________________

Eating Out

Lunch Menu

ABC soup	25¢	grape juice	8¢	apple	9¢
pizza	35¢	milk	17¢	peach	7¢
burger	30¢	orange juice	14¢	yogurt	12¢

You have 80¢. You want to have at least 20¢ left after you pay for lunch. Show two lunches you could buy if you choose one thing from each group. Ring the one that you like better.

Pick 3 things.

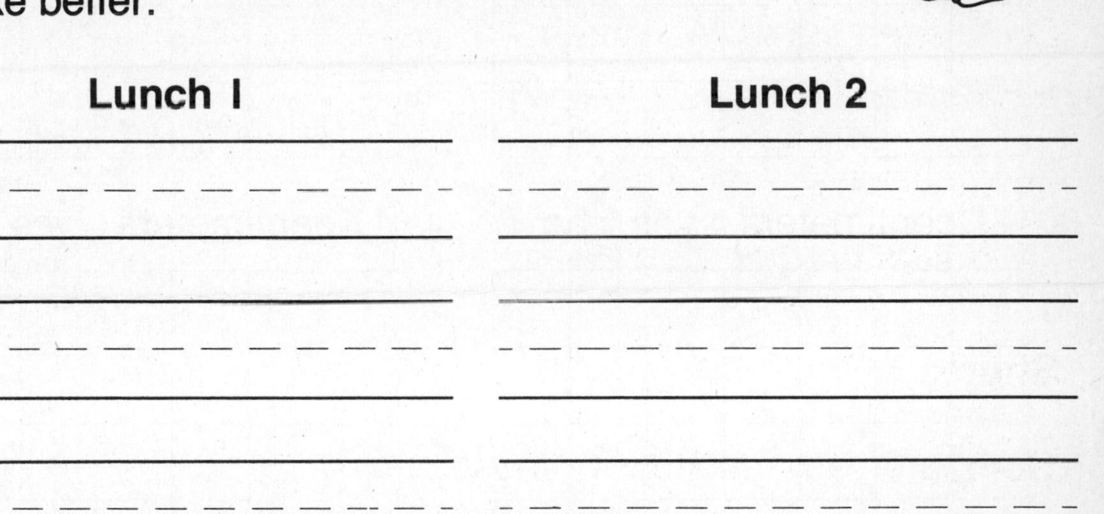

Lunch 1 **Lunch 2**

FOCUS: Students use personal judgments and computational skills to help make decisions.

Name ______________________________ **Number Sense**

Use with text pages 289–290.

Perry's Perimeters

Perry found some grid paper. Each small square is 1 centimeter on each side. Perry drew this rectangle. What is the perimeter?

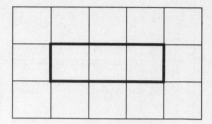

The perimeter is ____ centimeters.

Use the grids below. Try to draw a rectangle with the given perimeter. If you can draw it, ring *yes*. If you can't, ring *no*. Draw only on the grid lines.

1. 12 centimeters yes no

2. 16 centimeters yes no

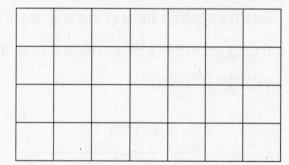

3. 11 centimeters yes no

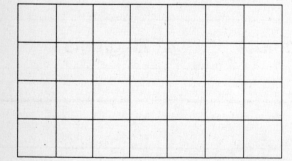

4. 17 centimeters yes no

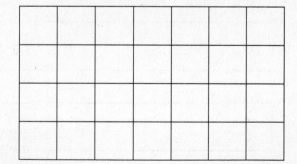

5. Draw a green rectangle with a perimeter of 10 centimeters. Use one of the grids above.

FOCUS: Students use their number sense to analyze and draw rectangles with given perimeters.

Name ____________________

Problem Solving

Use with text pages 299–300.

Measurement Mix-Up

In each problem some numbers are missing. For the first number, choose from the box a reasonable number that fits the story. Then solve the problem. The answer is not in the box.

23	75	$\frac{1}{2}$	2

HINT Use each number in the box just once.

1. Outside it was cold. At 5 o'clock the temperature was _____°C. In thc next hour the temperature dropped 2 degrees. What was the temperature then?

   _____°C

2. The house was gloomy, but it was heated. The temperature was _____°C. In the next hour it might rise another 4 degrees. What would the temperature be then? _____°C

3. Carl found a step ladder that was about 10 centimeters taller than his dog Rover. Rover was _____ centimeters tall. How tall was the ladder?

   _____ centimeters.

4. "Hey, Carl!" Ben said. "Look! I found the two paint cans that we need. Each has _____ liter of paint in it." How much paint in all was in the cans?

   _____ liter.

FOCUS: Students select reasonable numbers to use as data in problems and then solve the problems.

Name ______________________________ **Logic**

Use with text pages 305–306.

If, Then

Follow each direction before going on to the next one.

HINT You may have to both color *and* ring some objects.

1. • If the shape is a circle, then color it red.
   • If it is not a circle, then ring it.

 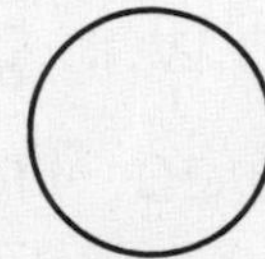 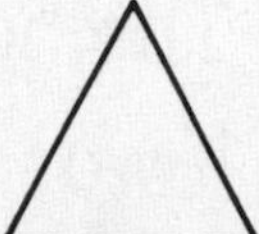   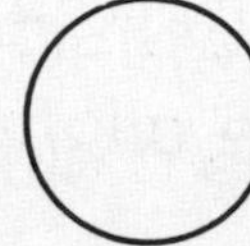

2. • If the shape is a square, then color it blue.
   • If it is not a circle, then ring it.

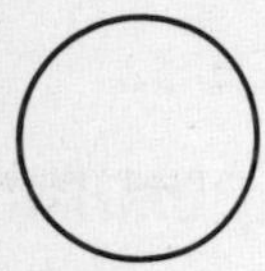  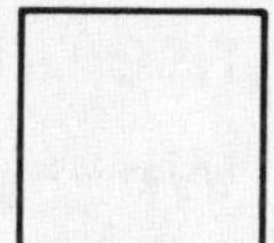 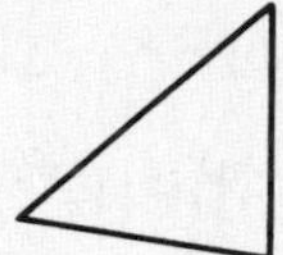 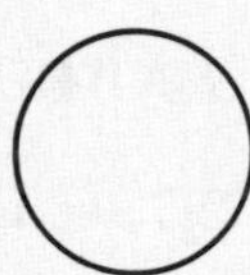 

Create Your Own

Complete the sentences for these shapes.
Give them to a classmate to solve.

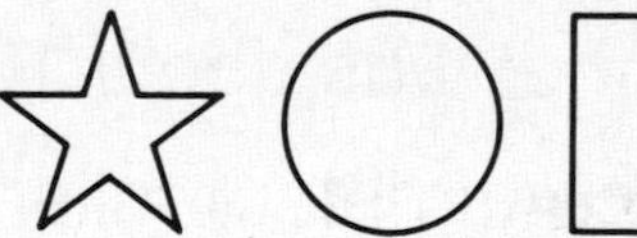

If the shape is a ______________ ,

then color it ______________ .

If it is not a ______________ , then ring it.

FOCUS: Students use logical thinking to follow *if, then* sentences.

Balancing the Scale!

Carla has these four weights. Draw pictures to show how she can balance the scale using all four weights. Part of the drawing is done for you.

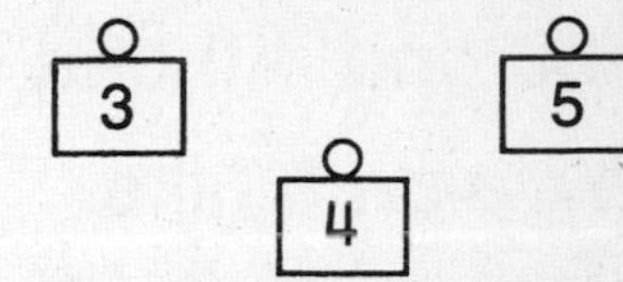

The numbers stand for different weights.

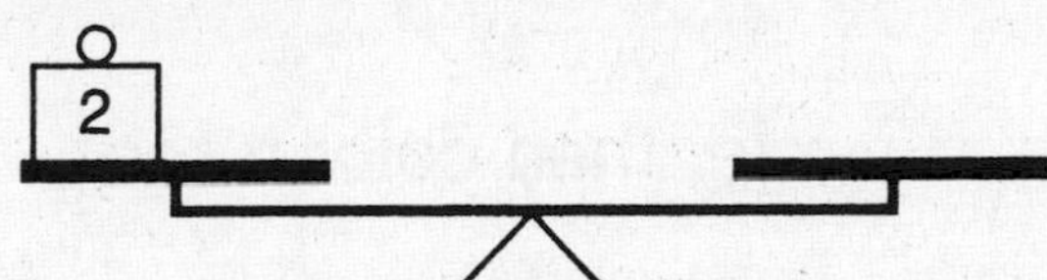

Draw to show how to balance the scale. Use all the weights.

1. 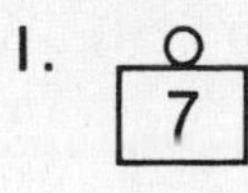

9 8 6

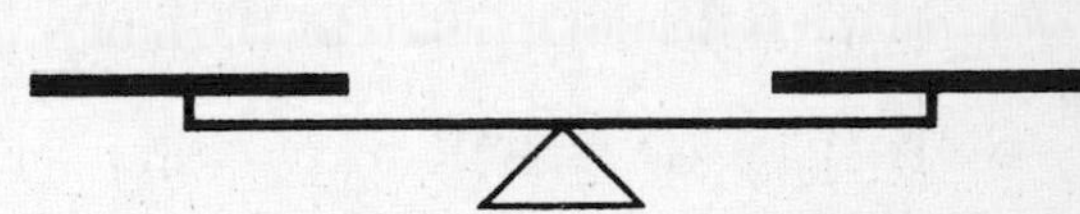

2. 

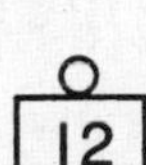

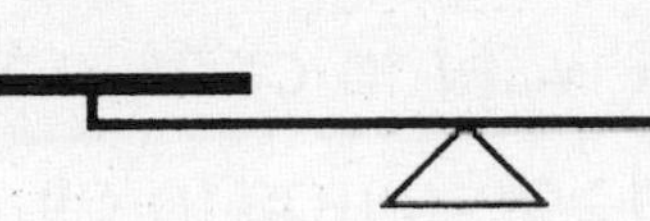

3. 

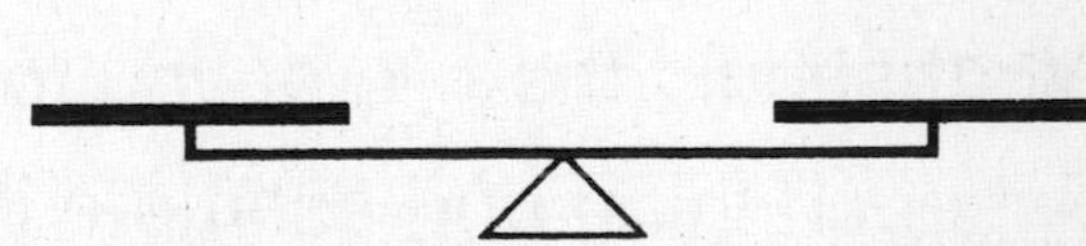

Share

Look back at the problems. Look for a pattern. Tell how you would balance the scale by using these four weights.

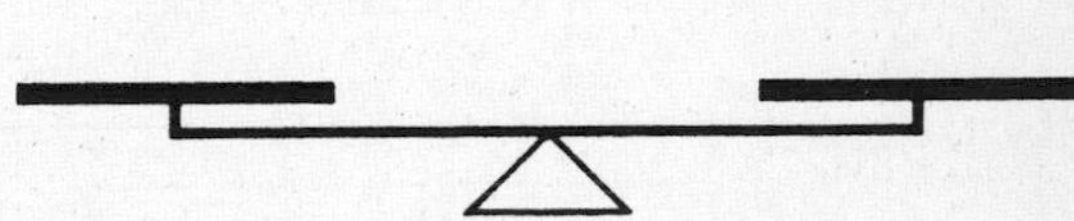

FOCUS: Students find a relationship involving equal sums for pairs of numbers in a group of four numbers.

Hiking

You and a friend are making plans to go on a hike.

A bag of nuts weighs about $\frac{1}{2}$ pound.

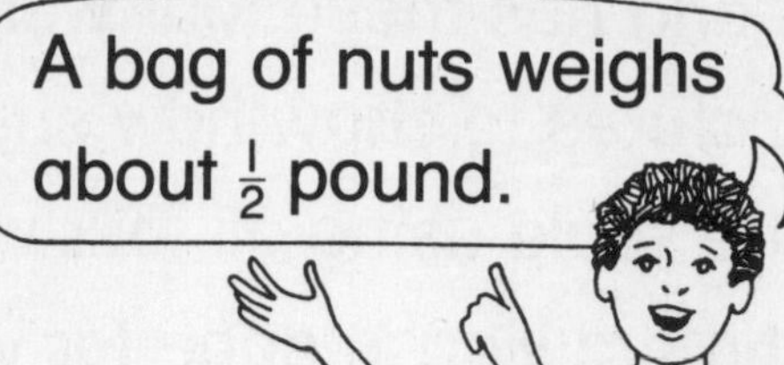

A full jug of water weighs about 2 pounds.

- You will hike for 3 or 4 hours in a park.
- The trails are well marked.
- There is no place to buy food or things to drink.
- You each have a backpack. The two of you want to carry no more than 10 pounds of things in all.

Three apples weigh about 1 pound.

My first-aid kit weighs about 1 pound.

What should the two of you take along? List each thing and estimate its weight. Try to find the total weight.

____

____

____

____

FOCUS: Students use personal judgments and estimation to plan what to carry on a hike.

Animal Parade

Beaver
65 pounds

Ostrich
300 pounds

Tiger
600 pounds

Giant Panda
350 pounds

Lion
550 pounds

Eagle
14 pounds

Use the picture and the information.
Complete each statement.

1. All of the animals weigh more than ____ pounds, but less than ____ pounds.

2. Some of the animals have ____ legs and ____ and some have ____ legs and ________ .

3. None of the animals weigh more than ____ pounds or less than ____ pounds.

4. ________ of the animals have names that begin with the letters *b, t,* and *l*.

FOCUS: Students use logical thinking to complete statements involving all, some, and none.

Name ______________________________ **Problem Solving**

Use with text pages 335–336.

Rock Collections

The children are carrying rocks in the boxes. The numbers tell how many rocks are in each box.

Read and solve each problem.

1. How many rocks is Tony carrying?

   ____

2. Who is carrying the fewest rocks?

   ____

3. How many more rocks is Marla carrying than Paul?

   ____

4. Which children are carrying more than 40 rocks?

   ____

5. Which problems did you solve by adding?

   ____

6. Which problem did you solve by subtracting?

   ____

FOCUS: Students solve problems and identify the number operation used.

Name ______________________ **Visual Thinking/Project**

Use with text pages 339–340.

Bigger and Bigger

Here is a drawing on grid paper. You can make a larger drawing like it. You can copy it on the grid below. Each square is larger than a square on the smaller drawing, so your drawing will be larger.

Work with a partner. Talk about making the larger picture. Talk about where the sun and clouds are in your larger picture. Each of you can make part of the picture, or each of you can do the whole picture.

FOCUS: Students use visual thinking, planning, and estimating to enlarge a picture.

Name ______________________________ **Visual Thinking/Project**

Use with text pages 339–340.

Bigger and Bigger

You can make a drawing of your own and then enlarge it. Plan a picture with a partner. Draw it on the small grid at the right. Then draw it on the larger grid below. When you have finished, color your picture.

FOCUS: Students use visual thinking and measurement skills to make and then enlarge a picture.

Name ____

Follow Those Arrows!

Maria made this number chart. Then she said, "I see a pattern on this chart. If I start at any number and move 1 space up, it's like adding 25."

Row 1	100	105	110	115	120
	75	80	85	90	95
	50	55	60	65	70
	25	30	35	40	45
	0	5	10	15	20

Maria wrote 5↑ = 30
20↑ = 45

1. Check Maria's pattern. Start with any number in the fourth row. Move 1 space up. Does the result fit Maria's pattern?

   25↑ = ____ 30↑ = ____ 40↑ = ____

2. If Maria moves 1 space to the right, it is like adding ____ . Test the pattern.

   5→ = ____ 10→ = ____ 35→ = ____

3. Study these patterns. Test them.

   0↗ = 30 10↗ = 40 55↗ = ____ 40↗ = ____

   0↗→ = 35 10↗→ = 45 55↗→ = ____ 50↗→ = ____

   25↗→ = 60 35↗→ = ____ 30↗→ = ____

FOCUS: Students discover patterns by making moves on a number chart.

Butterfly Net

Cut out the large square piece of paper. Fold it in half. Cut the folded paper to make the design. Then paste your cutout on another piece of paper. Color it.

Here's how I made this shape.

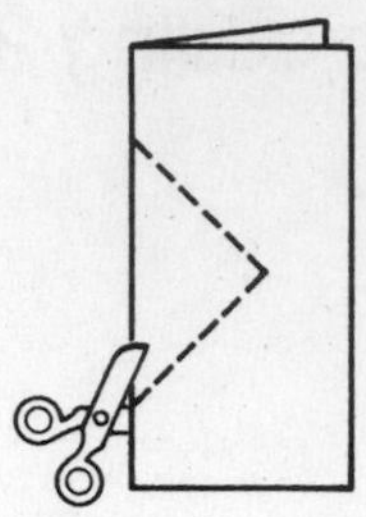

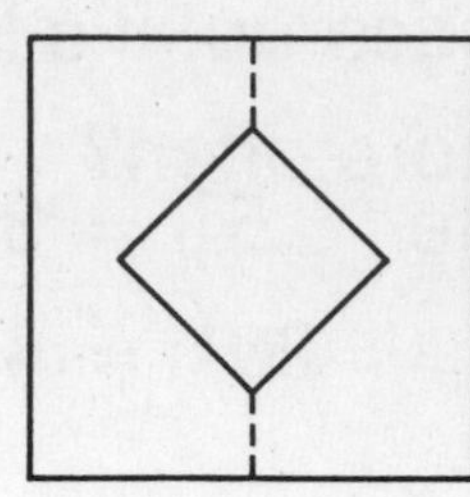

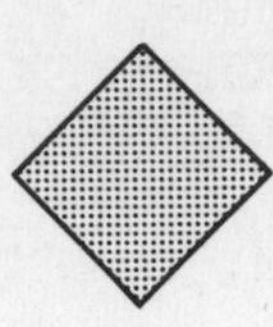

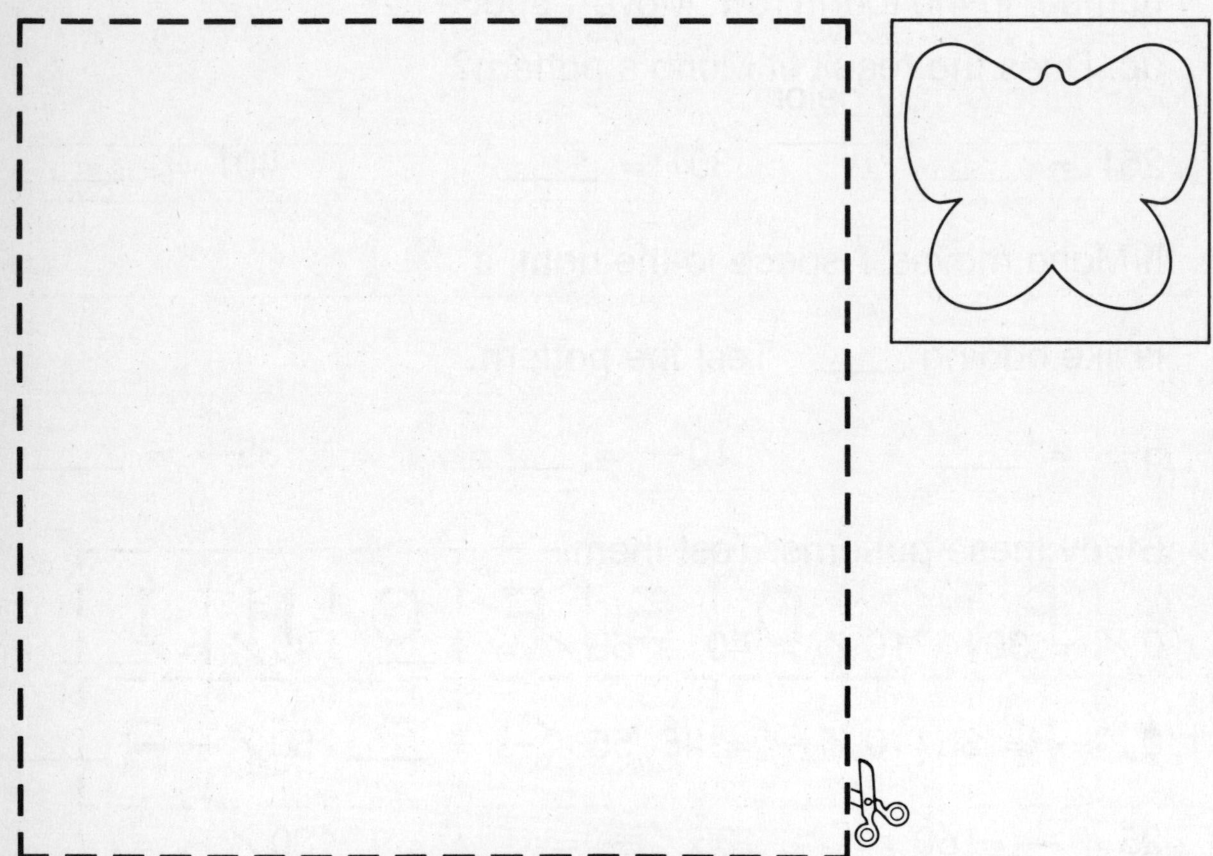

FOCUS: Students use mental imagery to create a design.

Name ______________________________ **Number Sense**

Use with text pages 355–356.

Alphabet Soup

Some letters are vowels. Some are consonants. Cut out the letters below. Place them in a bag. **What if** you pick 10 of them? Which type of letter will you pick more often?

Vowels
A, E, I, O, U

Consonants
B, C, D, F, G, H, J, K, L, M, N, P, Q, R, S, T, V, W, X, Y, Z

Ring your guess.

more vowels   more consonants

Now pick 10 letters. Write them in the spaces where they belong.

Type	Letters	Total
Vowels		
Consonants		

I drew more ______________________.

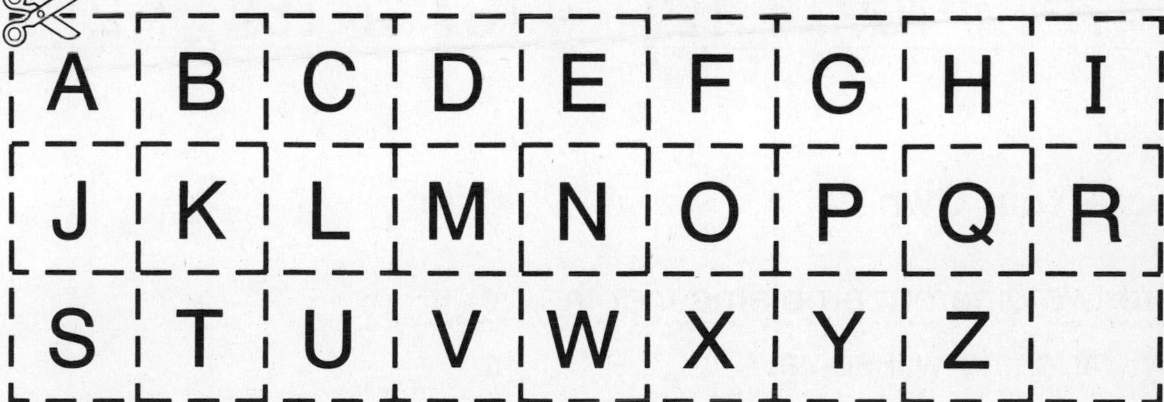

FOCUS: Students predict the probability of an event and show the results in an experiment.

Sum Machine!

Which sums can the Sum Machine find?

HINT Find the sums. Look for a pattern.

The Sum Machine will find the sum of these problems.

$$\begin{array}{r} 128 \\ +\ 427 \\ \hline \end{array} \qquad \begin{array}{r} 201 \\ +\ 132 \\ \hline \end{array} \qquad \begin{array}{r} 864 \\ +\ 135 \\ \hline \end{array} \qquad \begin{array}{r} 172 \\ +\ 50 \\ \hline \end{array}$$

It will not find these sums.

$$\begin{array}{r} 507 \\ +\ 215 \\ \hline \end{array} \qquad \begin{array}{r} 342 \\ +\ 469 \\ \hline \end{array} \qquad \begin{array}{r} 110 \\ +\ 87 \\ \hline \end{array} \qquad \begin{array}{r} 289 \\ +\ 605 \\ \hline \end{array}$$

Ring the problems that the Sum Machine will add.

$$\begin{array}{r} 305 \\ +\ 472 \\ \hline \end{array} \quad \begin{array}{r} 781 \\ +\ 109 \\ \hline \end{array} \quad \begin{array}{r} 434 \\ +\ 121 \\ \hline \end{array} \quad \begin{array}{r} 632 \\ +\ 137 \\ \hline \end{array} \quad \begin{array}{r} 734 \\ +\ 154 \\ \hline \end{array} \quad \begin{array}{r} 118 \\ +\ 215 \\ \hline \end{array}$$

Create Your Own

Write two different problems that the Sum Machine will solve.

FOCUS: Students use logical reasoning to find a pattern and use it to identify and write problems that follow the pattern.

Name ______________________________

Grouping Numbers

Study each group of numbers. Ring each sentence that describes the numbers. Then write another number that fits the group.

1. 235 150 105 175 355 ______
   - The numbers are greater than 100 and less than 400.
   - The numbers are all odd numbers.
   - The numbers all have 5 in ones place.
   - If I add any two of them, the sum will have 0 or 5 in ones place.

2. 166 376 264 346 136 ______
   - The numbers are all even numbers.
   - We say these numbers if we skip count by 2.
   - The numbers have 4 or 6 in the ones place.
   - All the numbers are between 150 and 400.

3. 363 633 533 343 233 ______
   - The digit 3 is in two places in every number.
   - The numbers are all greater than 100 and less than 600.
   - The digit 3 is in the ones place in every number.
   - There are 3 places in each number.

FOCUS: Students identify attributes of a group of numbers and write a number that has the same attributes.

Name ______________________________ **Number Sense**

Use with text pages 363–364.

Cora's Cross-Number Puzzle

Cora wrote a cross-number puzzle. It gives some of the answers and some of the clues. Write the rest of the answers and clues.

		A 1	5	B 2		C		D		E		F
G				H				I				

Across

A. The next number after 151

C. The next number after 960

E. 300 + 80 + 6

G. 2 hundreds 3 tens 8 ones

H. ______________________

I. ______________________

Down

A. 9 + 9

B. 35 − 10

C. 95 − 5

D. 9 + 3

E. ______________________

F. ______________________

FOCUS: Students use number sense to respond correctly to clues and to write clues for a cross-number puzzle.

Name ____

Square Deal

Copy the design. Color only the squares that should be shaded.

Start at the top. Work from left to right.

1.

2.

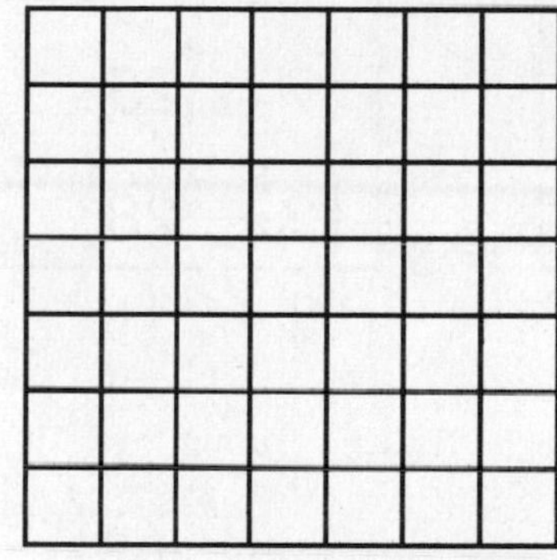

3.

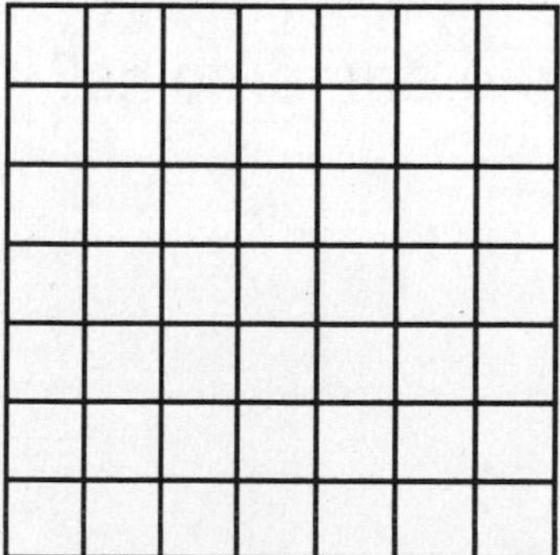

FOCUS: Students use visual imagery to copy a design onto a grid.

Name ____________________ **Number Sense**

Use with text pages 369–370.

Sixty-eight's

Make one path in each box. The numbers on the path should have a sum of exactly 68. Numbers must be joined by straight lines. You may use a calculator or paper and pencil to help you.

25	26	13
29	15	30
10	7	21

1.

22	4	18
6	20	14
12	30	26

2.

17	5	22
37	6	35
18	9	11

3.

9	7	10
18	24	16
4	6	26

4.

22	3	27
9	25	14
12	28	16

Work Space

25
+ 15
40

Share

Compare your work with a classmate's work. Did you find the same paths?

FOCUS: Students use number sense to solve a number search puzzle.

Name ____________________ **Decision Making**

Use with text pages 371–372.

Trip Time

You are traveling from Avon to Lyle.

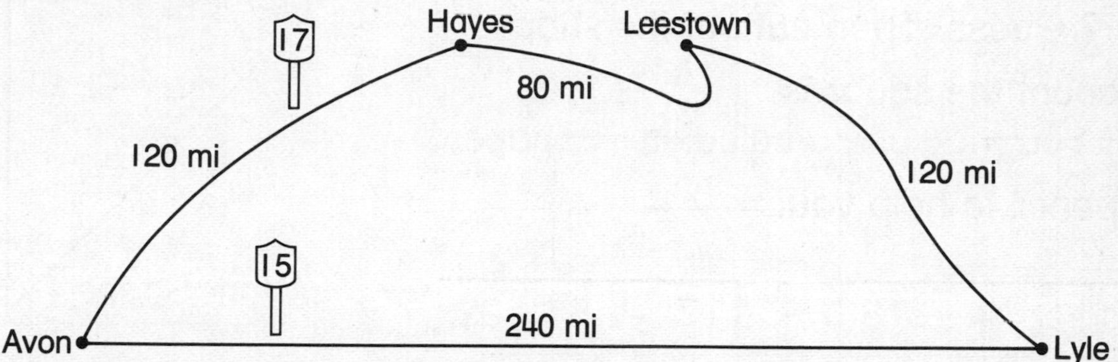

Use the map to solve these problems.

1. You went from Avon to Leestown in one day. How many miles did you travel?

   ____

2. The second day you went from Leestown to Lyle. How long was that trip?

   ____

3. What is the total number of miles between Avon and Lyle on Route 17?

   ____

4. How long is the trip from Avon to Lyle if you travel on Route 15?

   ____

5. How much longer is the trip from Avon to Lyle if you travel on Route 17 than if you travel on Route 15?

   ____

6. **What if** Route 15 and Route 17 were both good roads? Which one would you travel? Explain.

   ____

FOCUS: Students use computational skills to solve problems and thinking skills to form an opinion.

Name ______________________ **Number Sense**

Use with text pages 385–386.

Parts Make a Whole

How many grid boxes will each shape cover? Guess. Then cut out the shapes and count the squares.

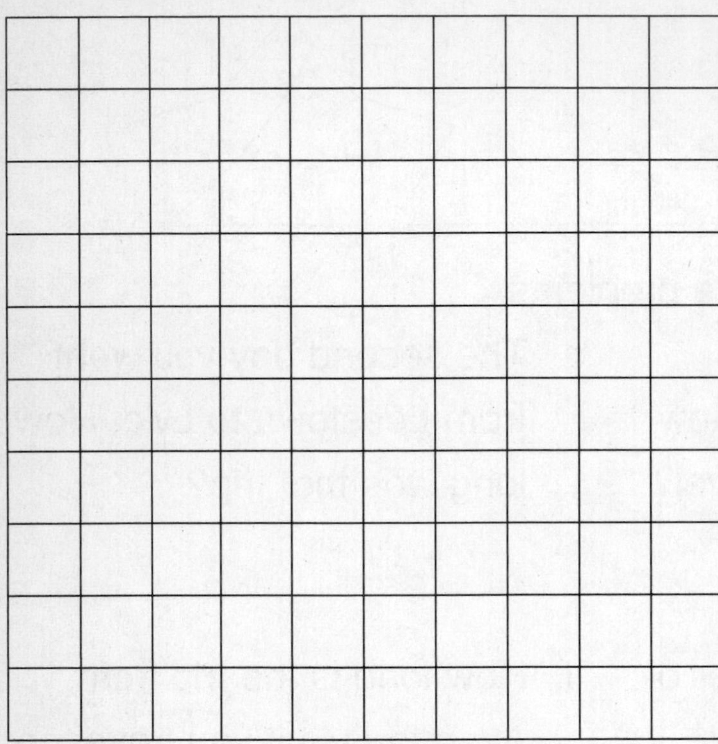

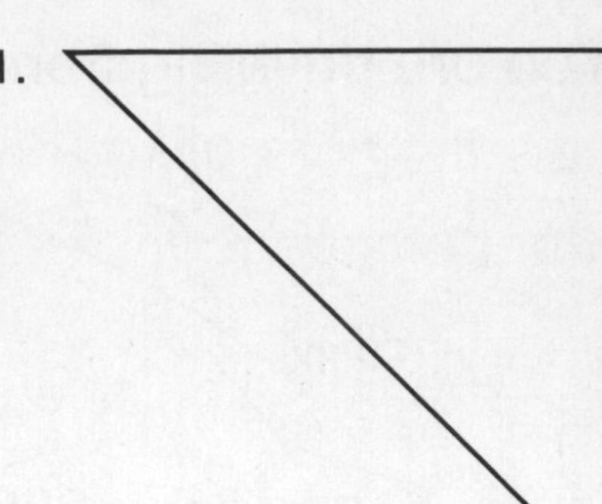

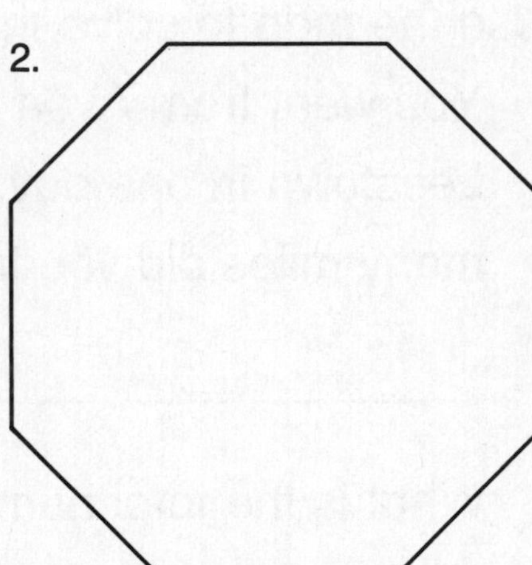

1. Cover boxes with △.

   Guess ______________

   Count ______________

2. Cover boxes with ⬡.

   Guess ______________

   Count ______________

Share

Tell how you counted parts of grid boxes.

FOCUS: Students estimate area and check their estimates.

Name ______________________________ **Relationships**

Use with text pages 387–388.

Look Alikes

Look at the numbers in each star. Decide how they are alike. Write another number that belongs to the group.

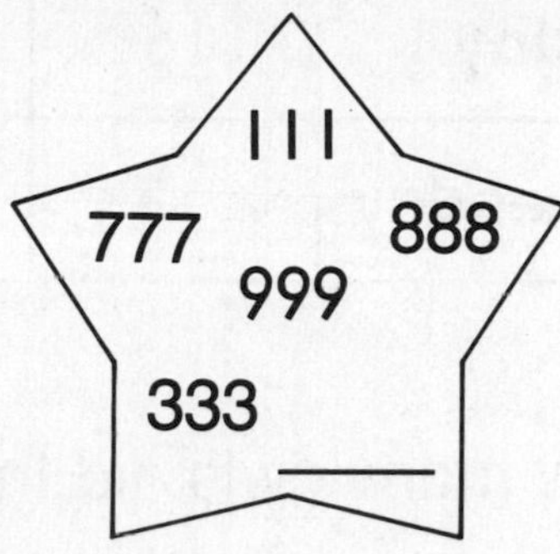

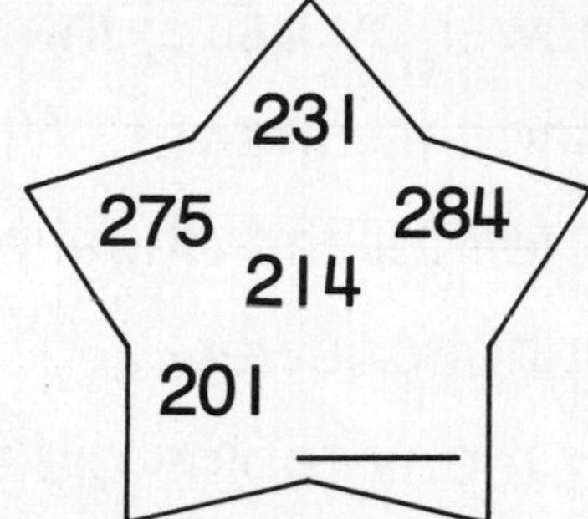

Make two groups of your own. Use these numbers.

12 35 45 18

16 65 14 85

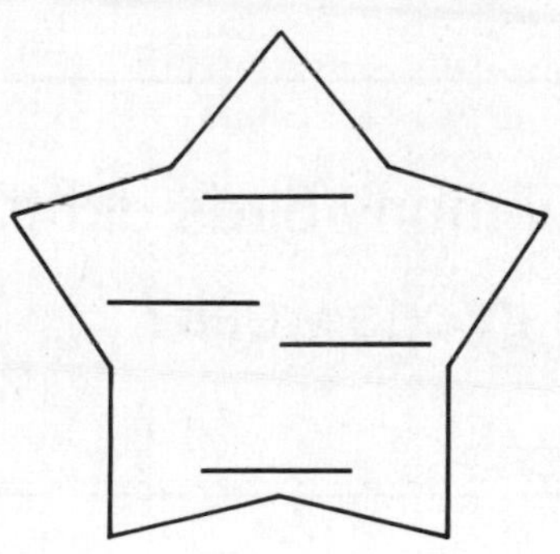

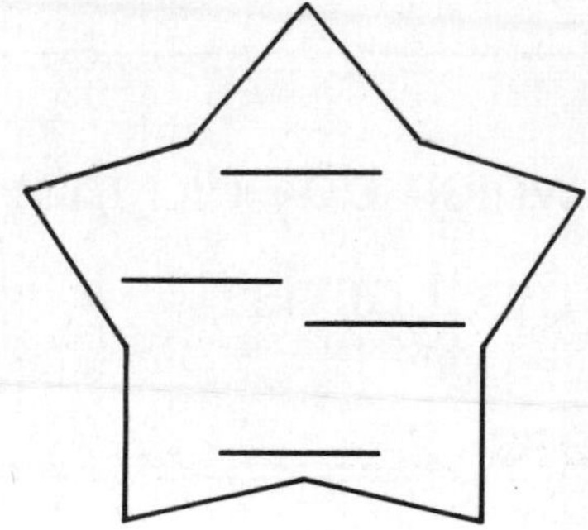

Share

Ask a classmate to give a rule that describes each of your groups and then add a number to each group.

FOCUS: Students determine the relationship that exists among numbers in a group.

Name ______________________________ **Problem Solving**

Use with text pages 393–394.

Watch the Birdy

The Bird Club members looked for robins and owls. Ring the questions that you can answer by using the chart. Then find the answer. Write *cannot tell* for the questions you cannot answer.

	Robins	Owls
Monday	7	22
Tuesday	16	15
Wednesday	3	4

1. How many robins did they see in all? ______________

2. How many owls did they see in all? ______________

3. On Thursday, did they see more robins or more owls?

____

4. On Tuesday, did they see more robins or more owls.?

____

5. On which day did they see the most birds?

____

6. How many birds did they see in one week?

____

7. What do you need to know to solve the problems that you cannot answer?

____

____

FOCUS: Students determine whether or not there is enough information to solve problems and tell what information is missing.

Name ______________________________ **Decision Making**

Use with text pages 395–396.

Free Time

You have exactly 60 minutes free. How would you spend the time? Write what you would do. Write the starting time for each activity. Pick five activities or some of your own.

Riding my bike
Doing cartwheels
Writing a letter
Going to the movies
Playing tic-tac-toe
Seeing a puppet show
Playing catch
Visiting the zoo
Drawing
Reading

My Plan

1:00 ______________________________

___:___ ______________________________

___:___ ______________________________

___:___ ______________________________

___:___ ______________________________

FOCUS: Students use their knowledge of time to decide on a schedule.

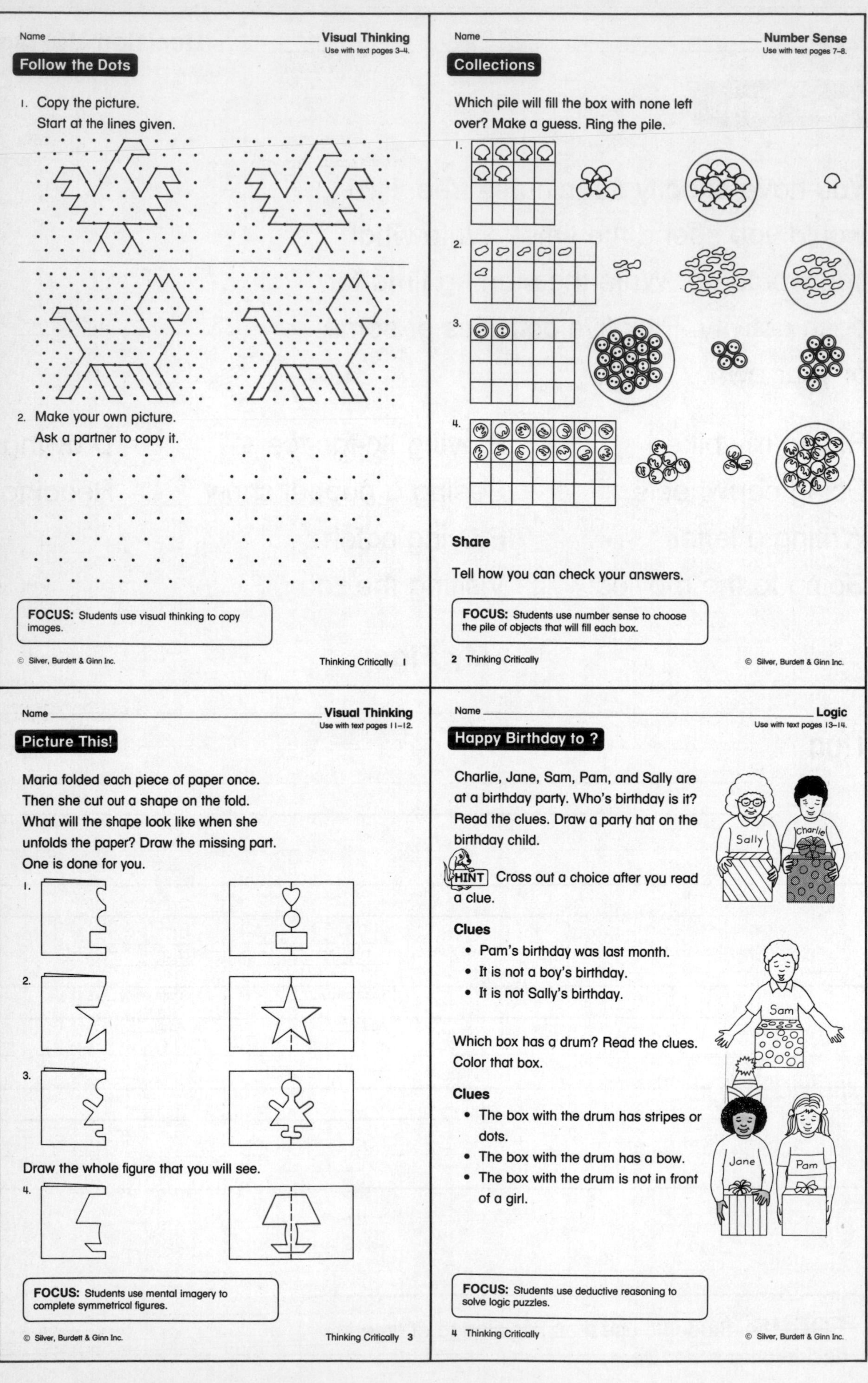

Name ____________________ **Visual Thinking**
Use with text pages 3–4.

Follow the Dots

1. Copy the picture.
   Start at the lines given.

2. Make your own picture.
   Ask a partner to copy it.

FOCUS: Students use visual thinking to copy images.

Name ____________________ **Number Sense**
Use with text pages 7–8.

Collections

Which pile will fill the box with none left over? Make a guess. Ring the pile.

1.

2.

3.

4.

Share

Tell how you can check your answers.

FOCUS: Students use number sense to choose the pile of objects that will fill each box.

Name ____________________ **Visual Thinking**
Use with text pages 11–12.

Picture This!

Maria folded each piece of paper once.
Then she cut out a shape on the fold.
What will the shape look like when she unfolds the paper? Draw the missing part.
One is done for you.

1.

2.

3.

Draw the whole figure that you will see.

4.

FOCUS: Students use mental imagery to complete symmetrical figures.

Name ____________________ **Logic**
Use with text pages 13–14.

Happy Birthday to ?

Charlie, Jane, Sam, Pam, and Sally are at a birthday party. Who's birthday is it? Read the clues. Draw a party hat on the birthday child.

HINT Cross out a choice after you read a clue.

Clues

- Pam's birthday was last month.
- It is not a boy's birthday.
- It is not Sally's birthday.

Which box has a drum? Read the clues. Color that box.

Clues

- The box with the drum has stripes or dots.
- The box with the drum has a bow.
- The box with the drum is not in front of a girl.

FOCUS: Students use deductive reasoning to solve logic puzzles.

Name ________________ **Problem Solving**
Use with text pages 15–16.

Missing Numbers

Each problem has some numbers missing. Think of numbers for each box. Write one number in each box. Use numbers from 0 to 10. Use counters or draw pictures to help you.
Answers may vary. Possible answers are given.

1. Maria has [3] fish. Ann has [9] fish. They have [12] fish in all.
2. Mike has [2] toads. Dot has [6] toads. They have [8] toads in all.
3. Al has [4] snails. Todd has [3] snails. Luis has [2] snails. They have [9] snails in all.
4. Jo has [3] turtles. Liz has [3] turtles. Candy has [4] turtles. They have [10] turtles in all.

Share

Tell a partner how you completed each problem.

FOCUS: Students discuss methods for finding missing addends in word problems.

Name ________________ **Decision Making**
Use with text pages 19–20.

Buying Stickers

You want to buy 3 or more stickers in each group. You can spend only 10¢, 11¢, or 12¢ for each group. Ring 3 or more stickers in each group. Then write their cost.

Answers will vary.

						Total Cost
1.	8¢	4¢	6¢	3¢	2¢	12 ¢
2.	2¢	3¢	5¢	4¢	3¢	___ ¢
3.	4¢	1¢	6¢	3¢	9¢	___ ¢
4.	9¢	7¢	4¢	2¢	5¢	___ ¢
5.	6¢	3¢	5¢	4¢	4¢	___ ¢

FOCUS: Students use mental math in a decision-making situation.

Name ________________ **Visual Thinking**
Use with text pages 21–22.

Puzzle Power

Talk about the kind of picture that would make a good puzzle. Check one.

- [ ] one little picture in each box
- [ ] one big picture that covers the whole grid

Why did you choose this kind of picture?

Make a puzzle. Draw a picture on the grid. Cut out the pieces on the dark lines. Have a partner put the puzzle back together.

Puzzles will vary.

FOCUS: Students use visual thinking to create and complete puzzles.

Name ________________ **Visual Thinking**
Use with text pages 23–24.

Building Blocks

How many blocks must you add or take away to make the wall in the box?

HINT Build with cubes to help.

1. Take away ___. Add 5.
2. Take away ___. Add 6.
3. Take away 6. Add ___.
4. Take away 4. Add ___.

FOCUS: Students identify the number of missing or extra blocks that are in a structure.

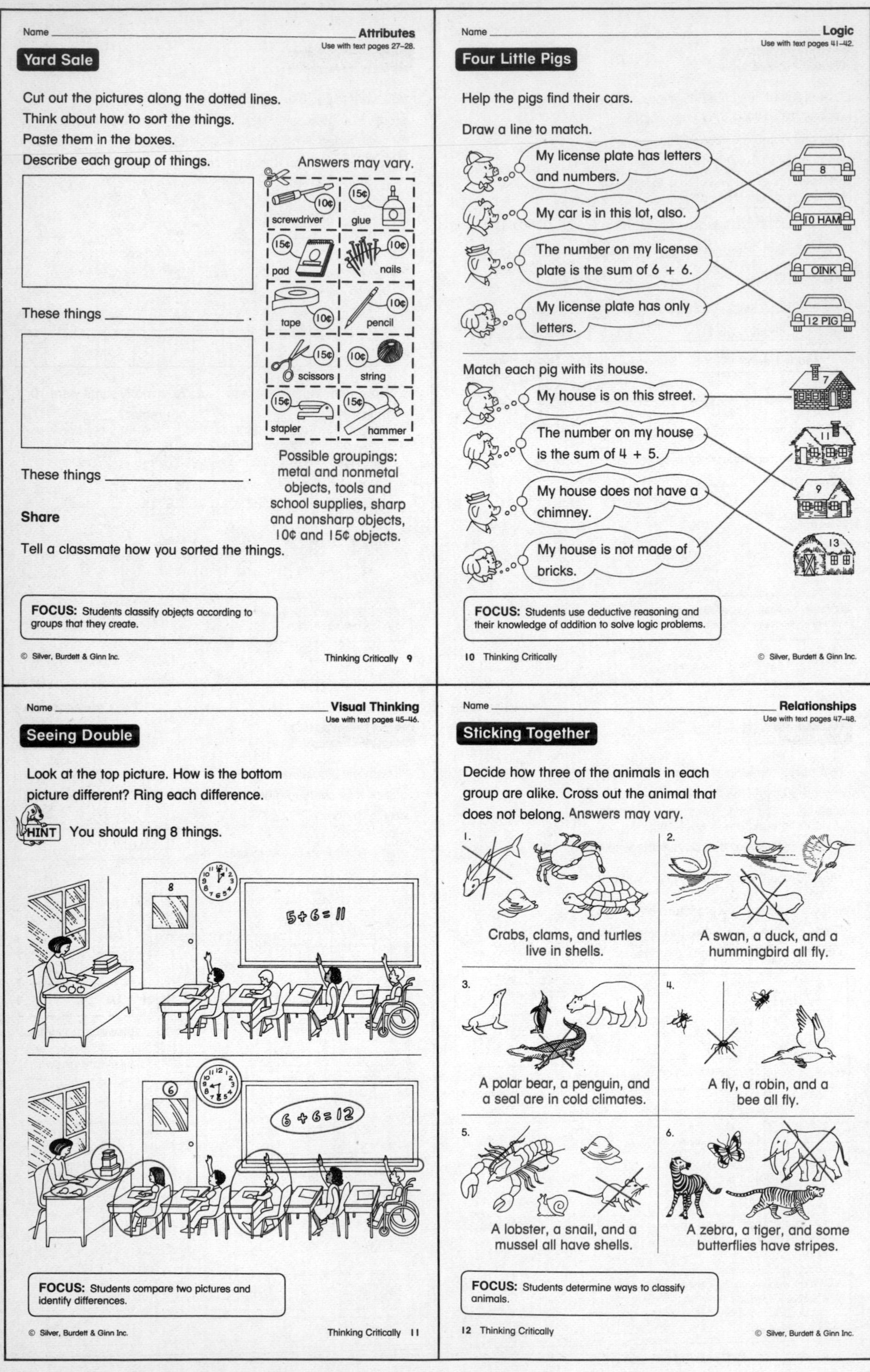

Name ____________________ **Attributes**

Use with text pages 27–28.

Yard Sale

Cut out the pictures along the dotted lines.
Think about how to sort the things.
Paste them in the boxes.
Describe each group of things.

Answers may vary.

These things ____________________ .

These things ____________________ .

Possible groupings: metal and nonmetal objects, tools and school supplies, sharp and nonsharp objects, 10¢ and 15¢ objects.

Share

Tell a classmate how you sorted the things.

FOCUS: Students classify objects according to groups that they create.

Name ____________________ **Logic**

Use with text pages 41–42.

Four Little Pigs

Help the pigs find their cars.

Draw a line to match.

My license plate has letters and numbers.

My car is in this lot, also.

The number on my license plate is the sum of 6 + 6.

My license plate has only letters.

Match each pig with its house.

My house is on this street.

The number on my house is the sum of 4 + 5.

My house does not have a chimney.

My house is not made of bricks.

FOCUS: Students use deductive reasoning and their knowledge of addition to solve logic problems.

Name ____________________ **Visual Thinking**

Use with text pages 45–46.

Seeing Double

Look at the top picture. How is the bottom picture different? Ring each difference.

HINT You should ring 8 things.

FOCUS: Students compare two pictures and identify differences.

Name ____________________ **Relationships**

Use with text pages 47–48.

Sticking Together

Decide how three of the animals in each group are alike. Cross out the animal that does not belong. Answers may vary.

1. Crabs, clams, and turtles live in shells.

2. A swan, a duck, and a hummingbird all fly.

3. A polar bear, a penguin, and a seal are in cold climates.

4. A fly, a robin, and a bee all fly.

5. A lobster, a snail, and a mussel all have shells.

6. A zebra, a tiger, and some butterflies have stripes.

FOCUS: Students determine ways to classify animals.

Name ______________________ **Problem Solving**
Use with text pages 51–52.

Toy Factory

Help the people in the toy factory. Tell how many buttons they need to make the animals. Fill in the chart.

HINT You may want to draw a picture, use counters, or use patterns.

Bunny Rabbits	Buttons
1	3
2	6
3	9
4	12

Teddy Bears	Buttons
1	4
2	8
3	12
4	16

Share

Tell how you found the answers.

FOCUS: Students solve problems by using computational skills, drawing pictures, using counters, or using number patterns.

Name ______________________ **Number Sense**
Use with text pages 55–56.

Tossing for Tens

Work with a partner. Toss two number cubes that show 1, 2, 3, 4, 5, and 6. Find the sum of the two numbers that come up. Do this 10 times.

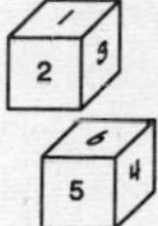

1. First, guess which will come up more often. Ring your answer.
   a sum of less than 10
   a sum greater than 10 Answers may vary.

Toss to find out. Fill in the chart as you toss the cubes. The first space shows the sum of the cubes above.

Toss	Try	1	2	3	4	5	6	7	8	9	10
Sum	1 + 6 7										

2. How many sums were less than 10? ____
3. How many sums were 10 or greater? ____

Answers may vary. Students should know that there are fewer pairs of numbers whose sum is 10 or greater.

4. Which different ways can the sum 7 come up? Show the different ways on the chart.

Cube 1	1	6	2	5	4	3
Cube 2	6	1	5	2	3	4

FOCUS: Students do a probability experiment and record their results in a chart.

Name ______________________ **Decision Making**
Use with text pages 57–58.

Fair Play

Welcome to the Fair. Find 4 different ways to use exactly 8 tickets. Write letters to show each choice. One is done for you.

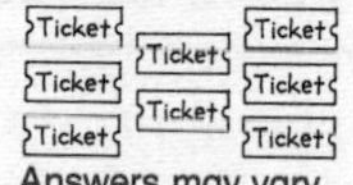

Answers may vary.

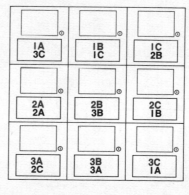

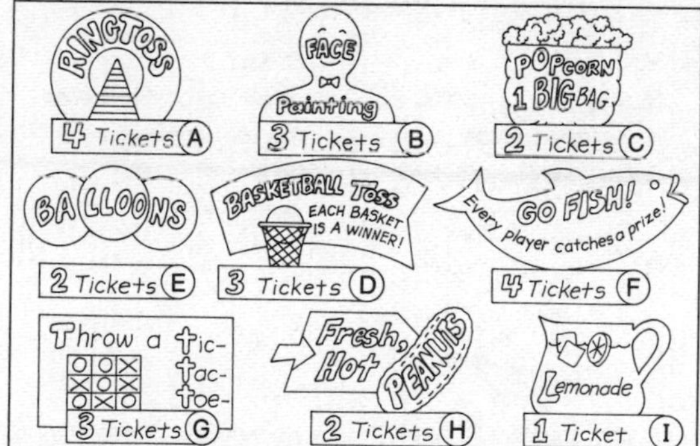

Choice 1: B, D, E

Choice 2: C, F, H

Choice 3: G, D, I, I

Choice 4: A, F

Also A, E, H; A, G, I; A, B, I; A, D, I; D, G, H; F, G, I, and others.

Ring the choice that you like best.

FOCUS: Students use their knowledge of addition and subtraction to make purchasing decisions.

Name ______________________ **Attributes/Relationships**
Use with text pages 69–70.

Mail Mix-up

The mailbox labels are not in a good order. Make the letter carrier's job easier. Paste the new labels over the old ones. Make a pattern.

1A 3C	1B 1C	1C 2B
2A 2A	2B 3B	2C 1B
3A 2C	3B 3A	3C 1A

3C	1B
2B	2A
3A	1C
2C	3B
1A	

Answers may vary.

Alternate answer:

1A	2A	3A
1B	2B	3B
1C	2C	3C

Share

Compare your work with a classmate's work. Did you order the labels in the same way? Did you both make the letter carrier's job easier?

FOCUS: Students organize labels in a useful way.

Name ______________________ **Number Sense**
Use with text pages 71–72.

Code Breaker

Do you know how to use a code?
Each symbol stands for a number.
Write + or – in the circle to make a sentence. Then decode the symbols and write a true number sentence.
One is done for you.

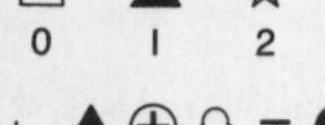

⌓	▲	☆	♥	⧖	◆	☁	☾	▽	■
0	1	2	3	4	5	6	7	8	9

1. ▲ ⊕ ☁ = ☾
   1 + 6 = 7
2. ■ ⊖ ☁ = ♥
   9 – 6 = 3
3. ■ ⊖ ☾ = ☆
   9 – 7 = 2
4. ☆ ⊕ ♥ = ◆
   2 + 3 = 5
5. ■ ⊖ ◆ = ⧖
   9 – 5 = 4
6. ▽ ⊕ ⌓ = ▽
   8 + 0 = 8
7. ☾ ⊖ ◆ = ☆
   7 – 5 = 2
8. ♥ ⊖ ♥ = ⌓
   3 – 3 = 0
9. ⧖ ⊕ ◆ = ■
   4 + 5 = 9
10. ☁ ⊕ ⌓ = ☁
    6 + 0 = 6

FOCUS: Students use number sense to determine the numerical values of symbols.

Name ______________________ **Logic**
Use with text pages 73–74.

Picking Pairs

Bev is following a rule as she puts these pairs of facts in her book.

4 + 5 = 9	3 + 3 = 6	6 + 6 = 12
9 – 5 = 4	6 – 3 = 3	12 – 6 = 6

Bev will not put these pairs in her book.
They do not follow a rule.

3 + 2 = 5	8 + 1 = 9	5 + 4 = 9
5 – 4 = 1	9 – 7 = 2	14 – 5 = 9

Ring the one pair that Bev will put in her book.

(6 + 7 = 13	3 + 5 = 8	5 + 5 = 10
13 – 7 = 6)	8 – 1 = 7	5 – 5 = 0

Write three more pairs that Bev will put in her book.

Answers may vary. A possible answer is given.

7 + 8 = 15
15 – 8 = 7 ______ ______

Share

Write the rule that Bev followed.

She chose only related addition and subtraction sentences.

FOCUS: Students use their knowledge of related addition and subtraction facts to make a generalization.

Name ______________________ **Number Sense**
Use with text pages 79–80.

Eyes Shut

What if you took one marble out of the box with your eyes shut? Ring the kind of marble that you would be most likely to pick.

1. 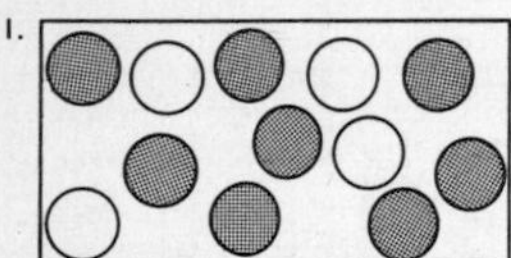 
2. 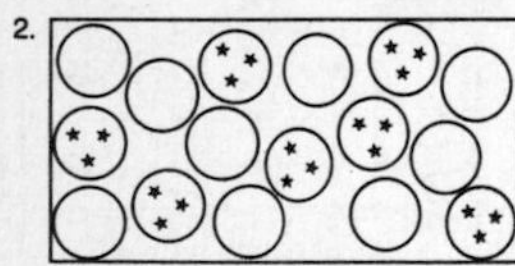 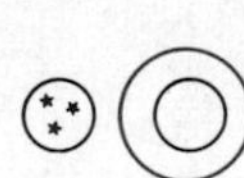
3. 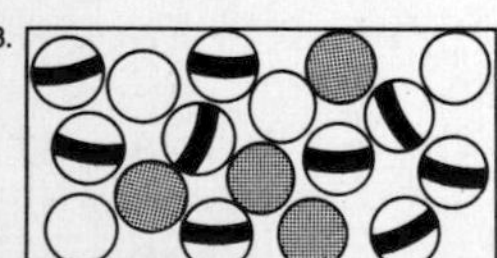 
4. 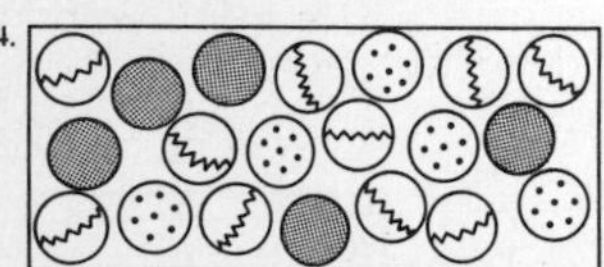 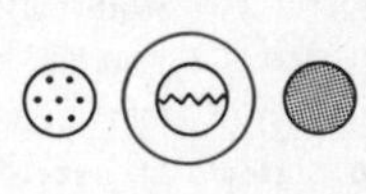

FOCUS: Students determine the probability of randomly selecting an object.

Name ______________________ **Problem Solving**
Use with text pages 83–84.

Creep, Crawl, or Fly

Read the problem. Ring the sentence that tells about it.

HINT Use numbers in place of pictures.

1. Rachel saw △ cows. Russell saw ○ horses. How many animals did Rachel and Russell see?

   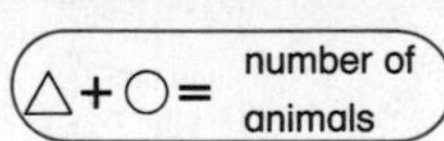

   (△ + ○ = number of animals)

   △ – ○ = number of animals

2. Russell saw □ beetles under a rock. ◇ beetles ran away. How many beetles were left?

   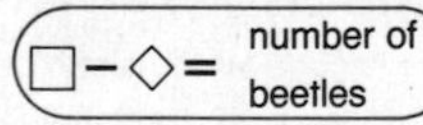

   (□ – ◇ = number of beetles)

   □ + ◇ = number of beetles

3. Rachel counted ☆ slugs. ✿ slugs went away. How many slugs were left?

   (☆ – ✿ = number of slugs)

   ✿ – ☆ = number of slugs

4. Rachel saw ☾ ants near a tree. Rachel saw ⊙ ants under a leaf. How many ants did she see in all?

   (☾ + ⊙ = number of ants)

   ☾ – ⊙ = number of ants

FOCUS: Students select a number sentence that represents a mathematical relationship in a word problem.

Name ______________________ **Visual Thinking**
Use with text pages 85–86.

Microscope Math

Tricia put the numbers 1 through 9, which she found in an old book, under her microscope. Write each number under its part. (None of the numbers are turned.)

Answers may vary.

HINT First, do the numbers that you are sure of.

1. 
3,8

2. 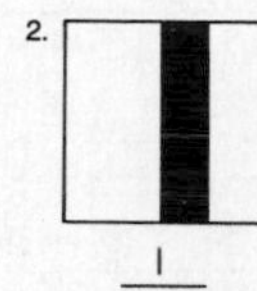
1

3. 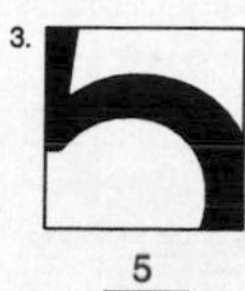
5

4. 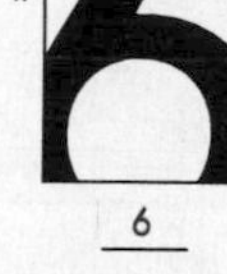
6

5. 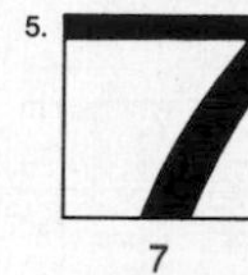
7

6. 
9

7. 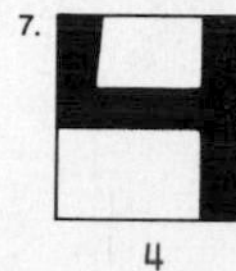
4

8. 
2

9. 
8

FOCUS: Students use visual thinking to match a part of a numeral to its whole.

Name ______________________ **Number Sense/Project**
Use with text pages 87–88.
Use masters 22 and 23.

Ready, Set, Grow

Planting Seeds

Read this problem.
One plant is kept in the light. One plant is kept in a dark place, such as a closet. Which one will have a longer stem?

Ring your guess. the plant in the light
the plant in the dark

Note: The plant kept in the dark will probably have the longer sprout, but the plant in the light will have more green leaves and stem growth.

Work in a small group to find the answer. Follow these steps.

1. Soak 4 lima beans in water overnight.
2. Get 2 clear plastic containers. Fill both containers with wet cotton or paper towels.
3. Place 2 lima beans in each container. Place the beans on the side of the container. That way you can see them grow.
4. Put one container in the light. Label it with the letter L. Put the other in the dark. Label it with the letter D.
5. Keep the cotton or paper towels wet.

FOCUS: Students set up a plant experiment.

Name ______________________ **Problem Solving/Project**
Use with text pages 87–88.
Use masters 22 and 23 together.

Ready, Set, Grow!

Measuring the Growth

Measure the stem of each plant on days 3, 6, and 9. Use a red ribbon to measure the plant grown in the light. Use a blue ribbon to measure the one kept in the dark. Cut each ribbon as long as each stem that you are measuring. Tape each ribbon on the table. The letter L stands for the plant grown in the light. The letter D stands for the plant that you kept in the dark.

HEIGHTS OF PLANTS

Day 3		Day 6		Day 9	
L	D	L	D	L	D

L = Light D = Dark

Share

After day 9, talk about what you see. Which stem is longer? Tell why you think this happened.

Plants need sunlight to grow.

Note: Each student group will need two clear plastic containers, four lima beans, cotton or paper towels, some red ribbon and blue ribbon, scissors, tape, and water. (Stripes of colored paper may be used instead of ribbons.) Have each group label its containers. (Do not put plants in direct sunlight.)

FOCUS: Students do an experiment to determine the better conditions for plant growth and to measure plants to the nearest whole centimeter.

Name ______________________ **Visual Thinking**
Use with text pages 99–100.

Ins and Outs

Look at each pond. Find the fish.
Draw three more fish in each pond.
Draw two flowers outside each pond.

HINT Color the pond if you need help.

Answers will vary.

1. 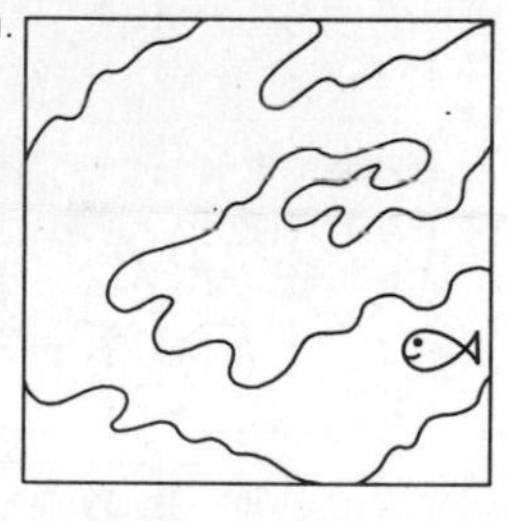

2. 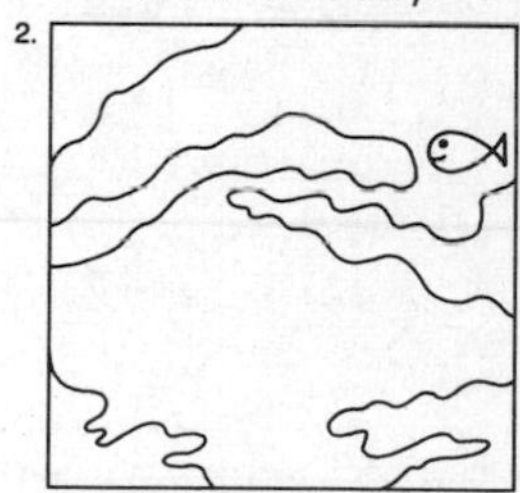

3. 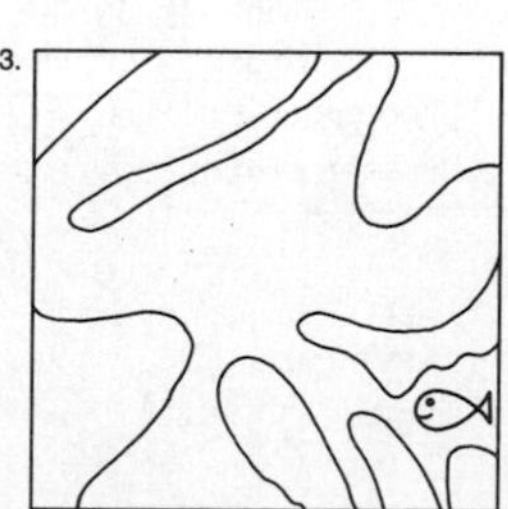

4. 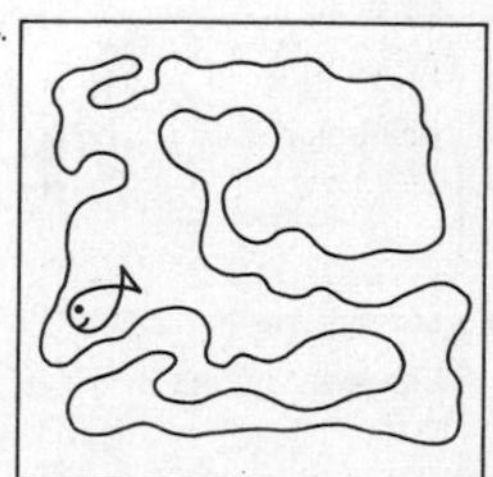

FOCUS: Students identify the inside and outside regions of figures.

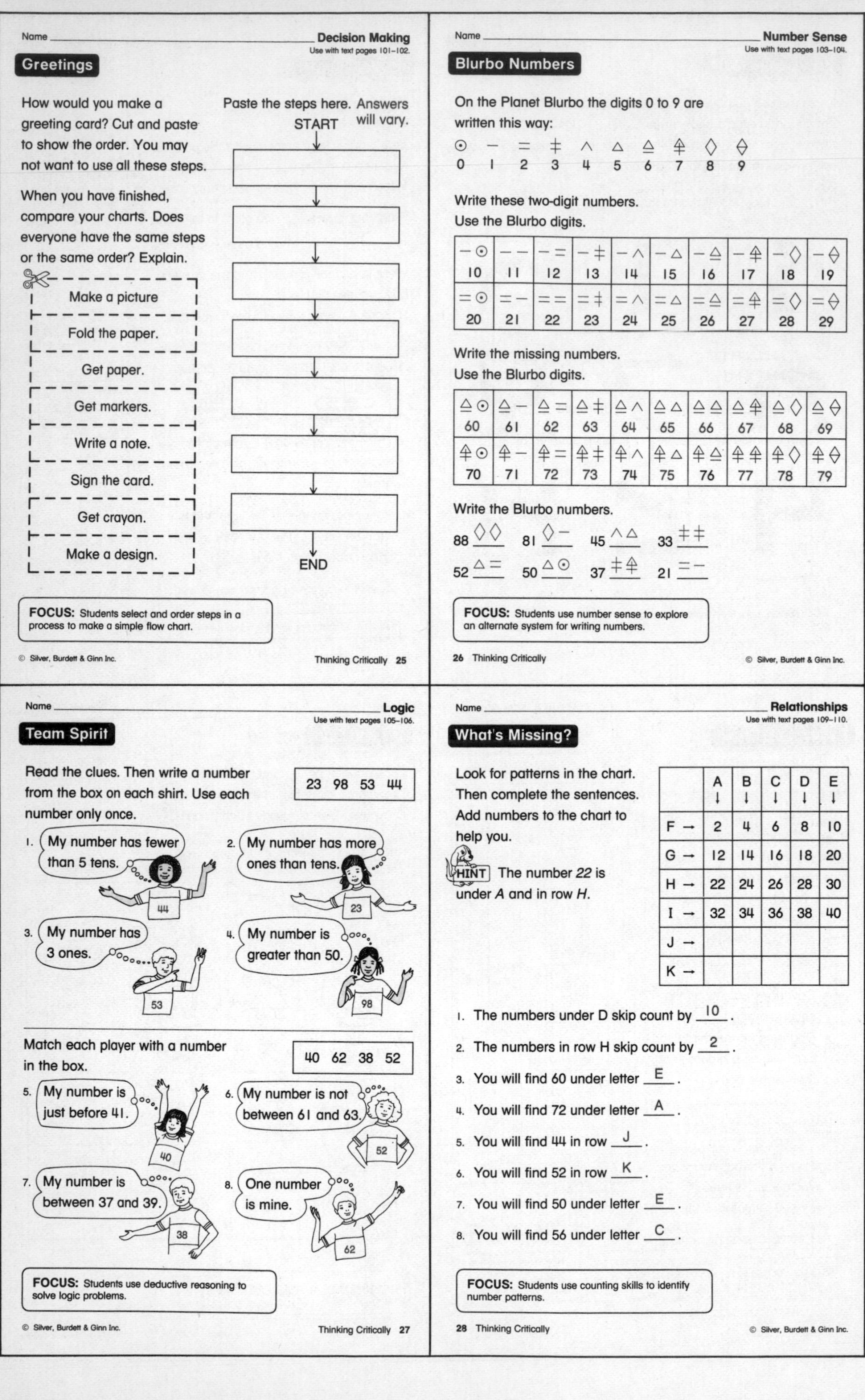

Name ______________ **Decision Making**

Use with text pages 101–102.

Greetings

How would you make a greeting card? Cut and paste to show the order. You may not want to use all these steps.

When you have finished, compare your charts. Does everyone have the same steps or the same order? Explain.

- Make a picture
- Fold the paper.
- Get paper.
- Get markers.
- Write a note.
- Sign the card.
- Get crayon.
- Make a design.

Paste the steps here. Answers will vary.

START → [ ] → [ ] → [ ] → [ ] → [ ] → [ ] → [ ] → END

FOCUS: Students select and order steps in a process to make a simple flow chart.

© Silver, Burdett & Ginn Inc. Thinking Critically 25

Name ______________ **Number Sense**

Use with text pages 103–104.

Blurbo Numbers

On the Planet Blurbo the digits 0 to 9 are written this way:

⊙	−	=	‡	∧	△	⍙	⍋	◇	⟠
0	1	2	3	4	5	6	7	8	9

Write these two-digit numbers. Use the Blurbo digits.

−⊙	−−	−=	−‡	−∧	−△	−⍙	−⍋	−◇	−⟠
10	11	12	13	14	15	16	17	18	19
=⊙	=−	==	=‡	=∧	=△	=⍙	=⍋	=◇	=⟠
20	21	22	23	24	25	26	27	28	29

Write the missing numbers. Use the Blurbo digits.

⍙⊙	⍙−	⍙=	⍙‡	⍙∧	⍙△	⍙⍙	⍙⍋	⍙◇	⍙⟠
60	61	62	63	64	65	66	67	68	69
⍋⊙	⍋−	⍋=	⍋‡	⍋∧	⍋△	⍋⍙	⍋⍋	⍋◇	⍋⟠
70	71	72	73	74	75	76	77	78	79

Write the Blurbo numbers.

88 ◇◇ 81 ◇− 45 ∧△ 33 ‡‡

52 △= 50 △⊙ 37 ‡⍋ 21 =−

FOCUS: Students use number sense to explore an alternate system for writing numbers.

26 Thinking Critically © Silver, Burdett & Ginn Inc.

Name ______________ **Logic**

Use with text pages 105–106.

Team Spirit

Read the clues. Then write a number from the box on each shirt. Use each number only once.

23 98 53 44

1. My number has fewer than 5 tens. — 44
2. My number has more ones than tens. — 23
3. My number has 3 ones. — 53
4. My number is greater than 50. — 98

Match each player with a number in the box.

40 62 38 52

5. My number is just before 41. — 40
6. My number is not between 61 and 63. — 52
7. My number is between 37 and 39. — 38
8. One number is mine. — 62

FOCUS: Students use deductive reasoning to solve logic problems.

© Silver, Burdett & Ginn Inc. Thinking Critically 27

Name ______________ **Relationships**

Use with text pages 109–110.

What's Missing?

Look for patterns in the chart. Then complete the sentences. Add numbers to the chart to help you.

HINT The number *22* is under *A* and in row *H*.

	A ↓	B ↓	C ↓	D ↓	E ↓
F →	2	4	6	8	10
G →	12	14	16	18	20
H →	22	24	26	28	30
I →	32	34	36	38	40
J →					
K →					

1. The numbers under D skip count by 10.
2. The numbers in row H skip count by 2.
3. You will find 60 under letter E.
4. You will find 72 under letter A.
5. You will find 44 in row J.
6. You will find 52 in row K.
7. You will find 50 under letter E.
8. You will find 56 under letter C.

FOCUS: Students use counting skills to identify number patterns.

28 Thinking Critically © Silver, Burdett & Ginn Inc.

Name ______________________ **Number Sense/Numeration**
Use with text pages 113–114.

How Many?

Skip count to find out how many are in each group. Then finish each sentence.

HINT You may need to count part of each group by ones.

Ways of skip counting may vary. Possible answers are given.

1. 

There are 20 ★s.
I skip counted by 10.

2. 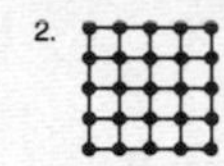

There are 25 •s.
I skip counted by 5.

3. 卌 卌
卌 卌 卌
卌 卌 卌

There are 40 ls.
I skip counted by 5.

4. 

There are 40 ls.
I skip counted by 10.

5. 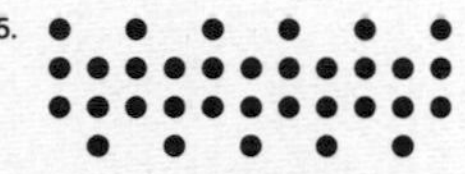

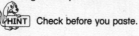

There are 33 •s.
I skip counted by 3.

6. × × × ×
× × × ×
× × × ×
× × × ×

There are 16 ×s.
I skip counted by 2.

FOCUS: Students use skip-counting skills to count objects in an organized way.

Name ______________________ **Decision Making/Problem Solving**
Use with text pages 115–116.

Shopping Trip

Ring the best buy in each row.

1. 

GIANT-SIZE
ACME
RUBBER BANDS
Just 59¢
50 in a box

GIANT-SIZE
ACME
RUBBER BANDS
On sale for 48¢
50 in a box

2. 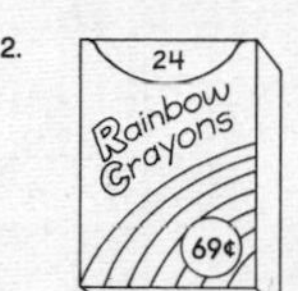

3. 

4. 

FOCUS: Students use their knowledge of comparing numbers to make a purchasing decision.

Name ______________________ **Logic**
Use with text pages 117–118.

Apartment for Rent

Read the clues. Cut out the pictures of the animals. Paste them on the floor in which they belong in the apartment house.

HINT Check before you paste.

Clues

- Goat lives on the first floor.
- Duck lives on the floor just above the fourth floor.
- Cow does not live on the second or the sixth floor.
- Dog lives on the third floor.
- Cat lives on a higher floor than Horse does.

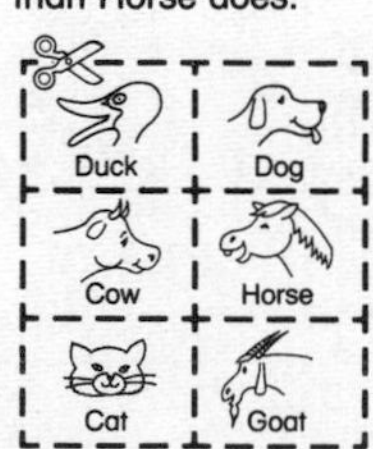

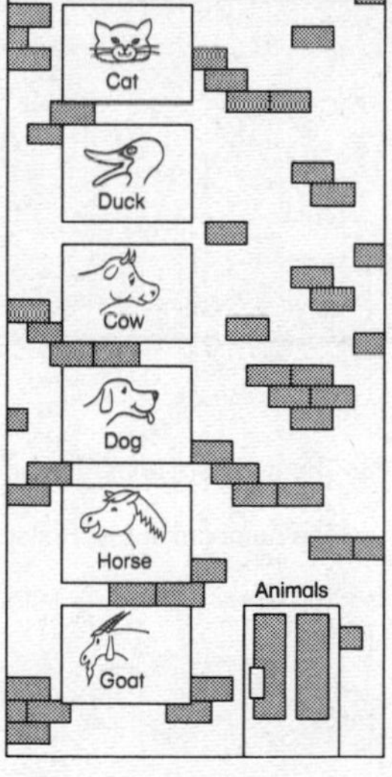

FOCUS: Students use their knowledge of ordinal numbers and deductive reasoning to solve a logic puzzle.

Name ______________________ **Attributes**
Use with text pages 129–130.

Shoobeedoobie

These are Shoobeedoobies. These are *not* Shoobeedoobies.

Ring the Shoobeedoobies in each group.

1. 

2. 

3. 

4. 

Share

Tell how you found the Shoobeedoobies.
Shoobeedoobies have 3 eyes, 3 legs, and 3 fingers on each hand.

FOCUS: Students compare attributes to determine whether figures belong in a group.

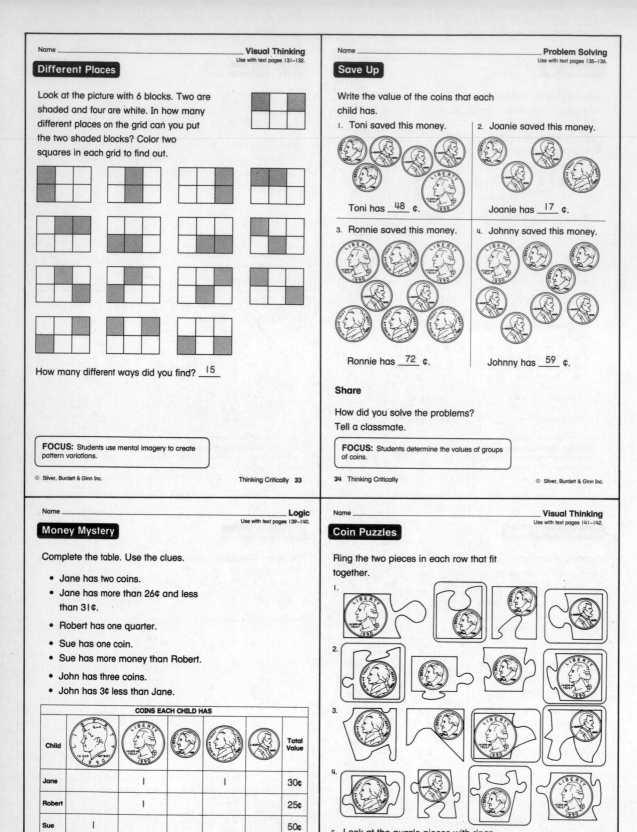

Name ______________________ **Visual Thinking**
Use with text pages 131–132.

Different Places

Look at the picture with 6 blocks. Two are shaded and four are white. In how many different places on the grid can you put the two shaded blocks? Color two squares in each grid to find out.

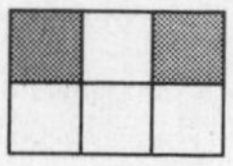

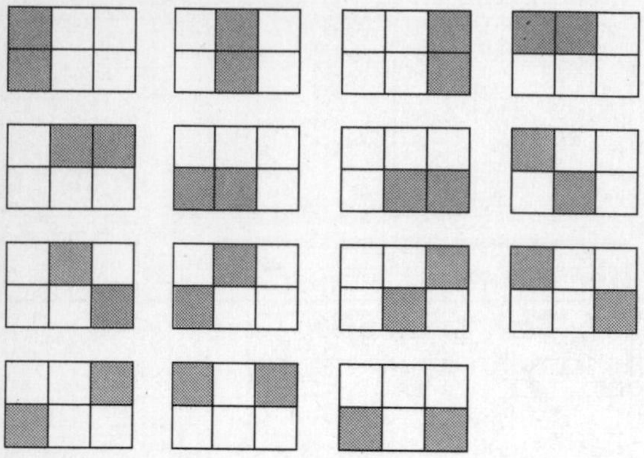

How many different ways did you find? 15

FOCUS: Students use mental imagery to create pattern variations.

Name ______________________ **Problem Solving**
Use with text pages 135–136.

Save Up

Write the value of the coins that each child has.

1. Toni saved this money.

Toni has 48 ¢.

2. Joanie saved this money.

Joanie has 17 ¢.

3. Ronnie saved this money.

Ronnie has 72 ¢.

4. Johnny saved this money.

Johnny has 59 ¢.

Share

How did you solve the problems?
Tell a classmate.

FOCUS: Students determine the values of groups of coins.

Name ______________________ **Logic**
Use with text pages 139–140.

Money Mystery

Complete the table. Use the clues.

- Jane has two coins.
- Jane has more than 26¢ and less than 31¢.
- Robert has one quarter.
- Sue has one coin.
- Sue has more money than Robert.
- John has three coins.
- John has 3¢ less than Jane.

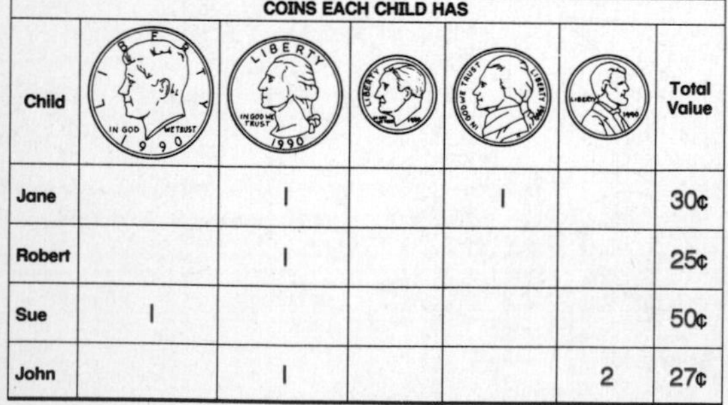

COINS EACH CHILD HAS

Child						Total Value
Jane		1		1		30¢
Robert		1				25¢
Sue	1					50¢
John		1			2	27¢

FOCUS: Students use deductive reasoning to solve a logic puzzle.

Name ______________________ **Visual Thinking**
Use with text pages 141–142.

Coin Puzzles

Ring the two pieces in each row that fit together.

1.

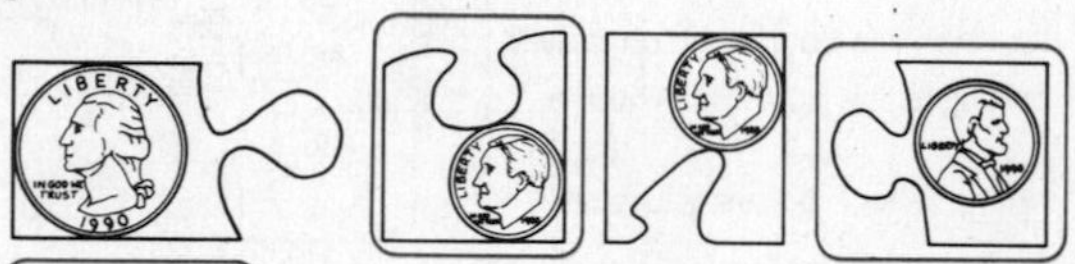

2.

3.

4.

5. Look at the puzzle pieces with rings.

How much are the coins worth? 82 ¢

Compare your answer with a classmate's.

FOCUS: Students use visual sense to match pairs of puzzle pieces and use their knowledge of money to check their answers.

Name ________ **Decision Making/Project**
Use with text pages 143–144.

Open for Business

Work with three other classmates. Make plans to run a store or other business. Follow these steps.

Plans will vary.

1. Decide what kind of business you will have. Ring one of these or write the name of another one.
   restaurant fruit store
   toy store book store
2. Think of a name for your store. Plan a sign for it. Draw it across the top of a large sheet of paper. Make it part of a poster.
3. Plan large posters to show what you would sell. Look in magazines or catalogs. Cut out 6 or more things that you would sell. Paste them on a large sheet of paper. You could also draw pictures. See the samples on page 38.
4. Make price tags. Cut out those on page 38 and write the correct prices on them. Paste the price tags next to each picture. Write prices from 1¢ to 50¢.

FOCUS: Students make decisions as they plan a play store and then make change as they make purchases.

Name ________ **Decision Making/Project**
Use with text pages 143–144.

Open for Business

Work with your group. Use punchout money and take turns as you shop at the store you pictured.

When you make change, remember to do this.

- Say the cost of the thing being bought.
- As you give back the coins, count up to the amount of money you were given.

Have fun as you shop. Change places with classmates in other groups and shop by using their posters.

___ ¢	___ ¢	___ ¢
___ ¢	___ ¢	___ ¢
___ ¢	___ ¢	___ ¢
___ ¢	___ ¢	___ ¢
___ ¢	___ ¢	___ ¢
___ ¢	___ ¢	___ ¢
___ ¢	___ ¢	___ ¢

FOCUS: Students make decisions as they plan a play store and then make change as they make purchases.

Note: Students will need old magazines, store advertisements, scissors, and paste. Provide large sheets of construction paper and punchout toy money.

Name ________ **Relationships**
Use with text pages 159–160.

Dot to Dot

Continue each pattern.

1.
2.
3.

Create Your Own

Create your own pattern here. Ask a classmate to continue it.

Patterns will vary.

Copy your classmate's pattern here.

FOCUS: Students continue patterns on a dot grid and then create their own pattern for a classmate to continue.

Name ________ **Logic**
Use with text pages 161–162.

Farstar Money

In Farstarland, Foof used these coins to pay for toys.

☆, □, and ☽

Marcia used money like ours to buy the same kinds of toys. Look at what Foof and Marcia paid for their toys.

Toys Bought	What Foof Paid	What Marcia Paid
ball	☆ ☆ ☆	1 nickel, 1 penny
mouse	□ □	1 dime
balloon	□ ☆ ☆	5 pennies
car	☽ ☆	2 nickels, 2 pennies
jar	☽ ☽ □	1 quarter

Write the value of each Farstar coin in cents.

☆ = 2¢ □ = 5¢ ☽ = 10¢

FOCUS: Students use number sense and logic to deduce the value of units in an invented monetary system.

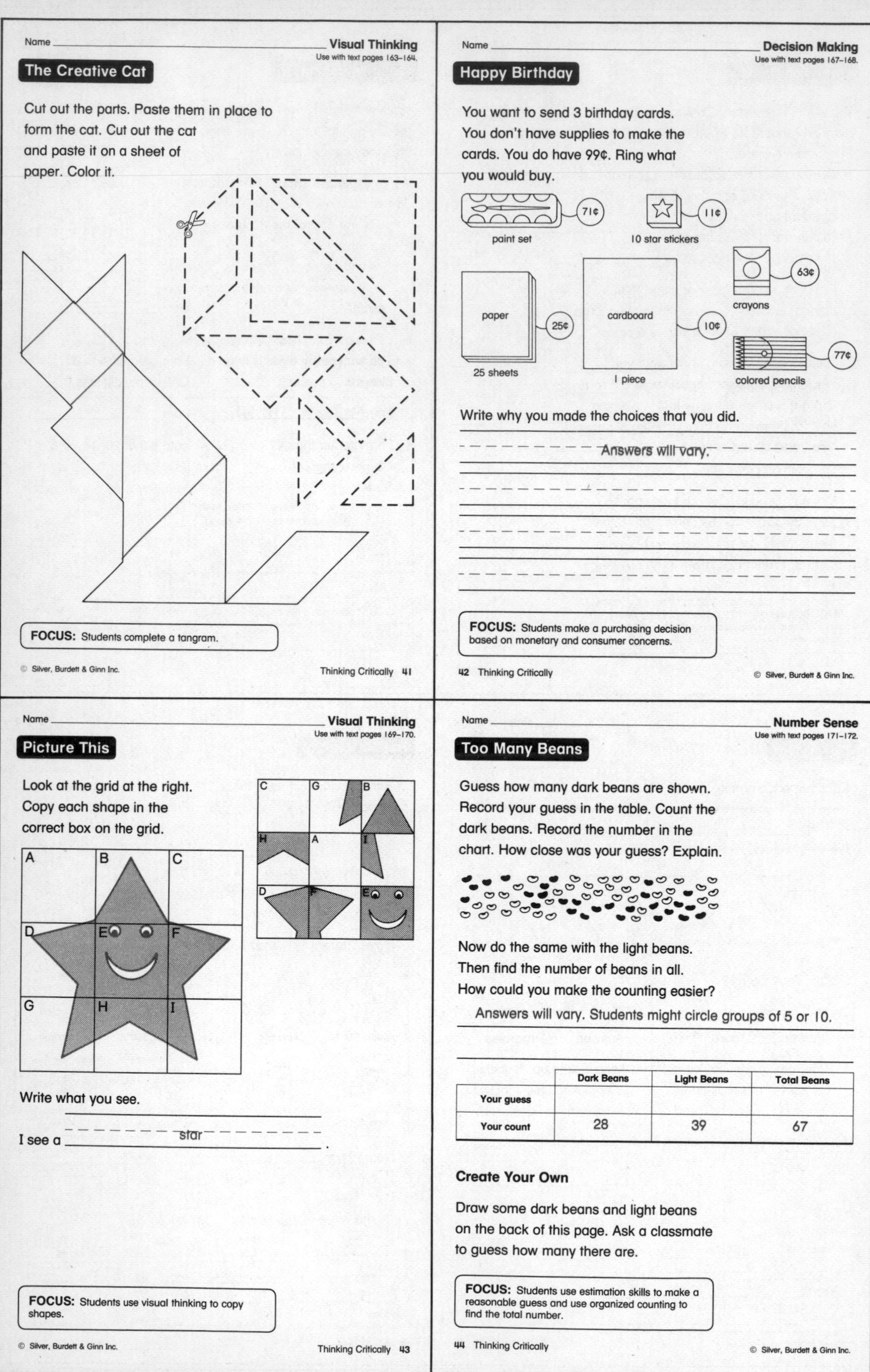

Name ______________________ **Visual Thinking**
Use with text pages 163–164.

The Creative Cat

Cut out the parts. Paste them in place to form the cat. Cut out the cat and paste it on a sheet of paper. Color it.

FOCUS: Students complete a tangram.

© Silver, Burdett & Ginn Inc. Thinking Critically 41

Name ______________________ **Decision Making**
Use with text pages 167–168.

Happy Birthday

You want to send 3 birthday cards. You don't have supplies to make the cards. You do have 99¢. Ring what you would buy.

Write why you made the choices that you did.

Answers will vary.

FOCUS: Students make a purchasing decision based on monetary and consumer concerns.

42 Thinking Critically © Silver, Burdett & Ginn Inc.

Name ______________________ **Visual Thinking**
Use with text pages 169–170.

Picture This

Look at the grid at the right. Copy each shape in the correct box on the grid.

Write what you see.

I see a star.

FOCUS: Students use visual thinking to copy shapes.

© Silver, Burdett & Ginn Inc. Thinking Critically 43

Name ______________________ **Number Sense**
Use with text pages 171–172.

Too Many Beans

Guess how many dark beans are shown. Record your guess in the table. Count the dark beans. Record the number in the chart. How close was your guess? Explain.

Now do the same with the light beans.
Then find the number of beans in all.
How could you make the counting easier?

Answers will vary. Students might circle groups of 5 or 10.

	Dark Beans	Light Beans	Total Beans
Your guess			
Your count	28	39	67

Create Your Own

Draw some dark beans and light beans on the back of this page. Ask a classmate to guess how many there are.

FOCUS: Students use estimation skills to make a reasonable guess and use organized counting to find the total number.

44 Thinking Critically © Silver, Burdett & Ginn Inc.

Name ______________________ **Number Sense**
Use with text pages 191–192.

Tally the Things

One tally mark looks like I.
Five tally marks look like ~~IIII~~.

Work with a group of 4 other children. Guess how many of each object your group has. You must be able to see the objects on the person or in the room. Then make tally marks to show how many. Next, write how many in all.

Answers will vary.

1. **Buttons**
   Guess: ____ Tally: [ ] Total: ____
2. **Pencils**
   Guess: ____ Tally: [ ] Total: ____
3. **Shoelace Holes**
   Guess: ____ Tally: [ ] Total: ____
4. **Red and Blue Crayons**
   Guess: ____ Tally: [ ] Total: ____

Share

Compare your totals with those of other groups.

FOCUS: Students use number sense to estimate and tally objects.

Name ______________________ **Logic**
Use with text pages 193–194.

Number Detective

Solve these math mysteries. Write the mystery number.

HINT When we write numbers, we use the digits 0, 1, 2, 3, 4, 5, 6, 7, 8, and 9. The number 94 has two digits, 9 and 4.

1. I am greater than 30.
   I am less than 40.
   One of my digits is 5.
   I am ___35___.
2. I am greater than 20.
   I am less than 34.
   The sum of my digits is 8.
   I am ___26___.
3. I am either 92, 27, or 78.
   The sum of my digits is less than 10.
   I am ___27___.
4. I am less than 79.
   I am greater than 61.
   One of my digits is 0.
   I am ___70___.
5. I am greater than 49.
   I am less than 60.
   Both of my digits are the same.
   I am ___55___.
6. I am either 20, 16, or 52.
   If you start at 0 and skip count by 5's, you will reach me.
   I am ___20___.

FOCUS: Students use deductive reasoning to solve number riddles.

Name ______________________ **Problem Solving**
Use with text pages 195–196.

Number Please!

12	14	35
17	8	28
7	46	

Replace each shape in a problem. Use the numbers in the box. Use each number only once. Then write the answer. The answers are not in the box.

Answers may vary. Possible answers are given.

1. Lisa has △ model cars. Her sister has ⬡ cars. How many more cars does Lisa have than her sister?
   △ = 17
   ⬡ = 7
   Answer: ___10___ cars
2. Meg had ᗰ marbles. Ann gave her ᗐ marbles. How many marbles does Meg have now?
   ᗰ = 8
   ᗐ = 12
   Answer: ___20___ marbles
3. Tim has □ baseball cards. Ed has ⇦ baseball cards. How many more baseball cards does Tim have than Ed?
   □ = 35
   ⇦ = 14
   Answer: ___21___ cards
4. Mike picked up ✳ jacks. Billy picked up ☾ jacks. How many jacks did Mike and Billy pick up?
   ✳ = 28
   ☾ = 46
   Answer: ___74___ jacks

FOCUS: Students choose sensible numbers from a box to complete word problems involving addition and subtraction.

Name ______________________ **Decision Making**
Use with text pages 201–202.

Soup Is On

What would you like for lunch? You have 85¢. Ring three or more things that you could buy.

Menu

soup 15¢	salad 20¢	fruit salad 25¢	apple 5¢
chicken 55¢	tuna 55¢	peanut butter 35¢	cheese 40¢
milk 5¢	orange juice 15¢	apple juice 15¢	juice punch 20¢

Complete the sentences. Answers will vary.

I spent ____¢.

I have ____¢ change.

FOCUS: Students use personal preference and price to make a purchasing decision.

Name ______________________________ **Attributes**

Use with text pages 203–204.

Sorry, Wrong Number!

Try to find a pattern in each row. One number does not fit the pattern. Cross it out. Write on the line the number that fits the pattern.

1.	7	17	27	~~36~~	47	57	67	37
2.	11	22	33	44	~~54~~	66	77	55
3.	5	~~18~~	29	41	53	65	77	17
4.	~~88~~	76	65	54	43	32	21	87
5.	3	6	9	12	15	18	~~23~~	21
6.	86	80	74	~~69~~	62	56	50	68
7.	94	93	91	88	84	~~78~~	73	79
8.	77	74	~~70~~	68	65	62	59	71
9.	20	40	60	~~50~~	100	120	140	80
10.	90	80	70	60	~~55~~	40	30	50
11.	13	~~27~~	39	52	65	78	91	26
12.	42	40	38	36	~~24~~	32	30	34

FOCUS: Students identify the number that does not belong in a series of numbers.

Name ______________________________ **Decision Making/Project**

Use with text pages 207–208.

Making Beads

Here are some directions for making a clay bead necklace. Number each group to show the order.

Making the Beads (Steps 1 – 4)

2 Make a hole in each bead for the string.

1 Form some clay to make beads.

3 Make a design on each bead with a toothpick.

4 Let the beads harden.

Finishing the Necklace (Steps 5 – 8)

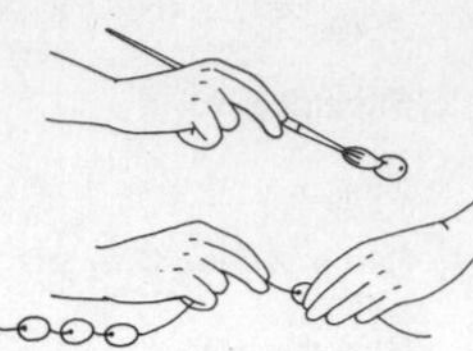

6 Let the paint dry.

8 Tie a knot in the string.

7 String the beads.

5 Paint each bead.

Share

Compare your list of steps with those of a classmate. Will you make any changes? Explain.

FOCUS: Students order steps required for making a bead necklace from clay.

Name ______________________________ **Decision Making/Project**

Use with text pages 207–208.

Beads

Part Two: Plan Ahead

Answers will vary.

Make plans for one necklace.

1. Draw the size bead that you want to make.

2. Write how many beads you want to make. __________

3. Weigh the amount of clay that you think you will need. Write its weight.

____

4. Cut a piece of string to fit around your neck. Measure the string. __________

Share

Share your plans with your classmates. Are any of your amounts too great? Are any too little? Make changes if you need to. Then make your necklace with your partner.

Note: You will need self-hardening clay, tempera paints, toothpicks, and fishing cord. Provide a scale for step 3. Ask students to bring their plans to you as you distribute the materials. You may wish to discuss unrealistic plans with students, or you may suggest that as they work they may want to change their plans.

FOCUS: Students make plans for making a necklace with clay beads.

Name ______________________________ **Logic**

Use with text pages 217–218.

Tick-Tock

Read the clues. Ring the watch or clock that fits all three clues.

HINT Cross out a picture after you read each clue.

- It does not have a wristband.
- It does not have a handle.
- It shows a time between 1:00 and 5:00.

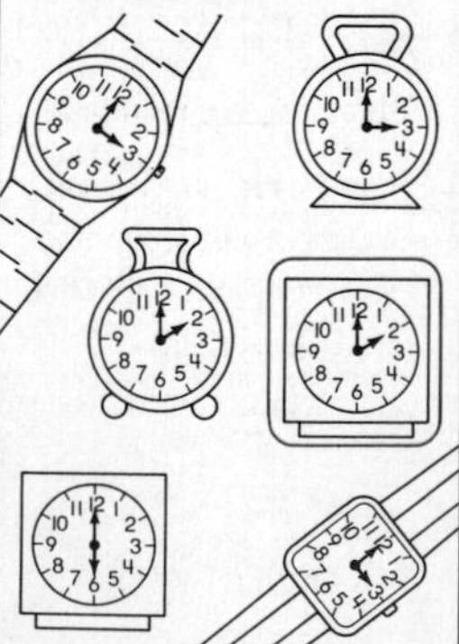

- It has an hour and a minute hand.
- It does not have stripes.
- It shows the same time as another watch or clock.

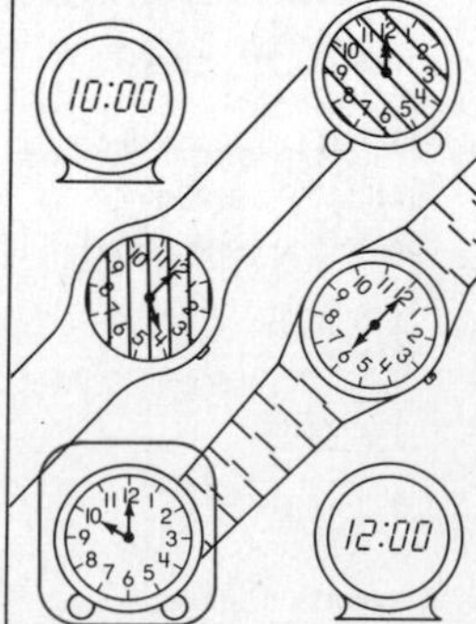

FOCUS: Students use deductive reasoning and their knowledge of time to solve logic problems.

Name ______________________________ **Relationships**

Use with text pages 219–220.

Patterns in Schedules

Each schedule for a class follows a pattern. Draw hands on the last clock to continue the pattern.

Schedules

1. Art classes

2. Dance classes

3. Tumbling classes

4. Music classes

FOCUS: Students use their knowledge of telling time to the hour to continue patterns shown on clock faces.

Name ______________________________ **Number Sense**

Use with text pages 221–222.

Make a Ten

Make the six cards shown here. Place them in a bag. Remove a card and write the number on the chart. Put the card back in the bag. Take 5 turns. If you score 10 or more, you win the game. See how many games you can win.

1	1	1
3	2	5

Game 1	
Turn	Score
1	
2	
3	
4	
5	
Total	

Game 2	
Turn	Score
1	
2	
3	
4	
5	
Total	

Game 3	
Turn	Score
1	
2	
3	
4	
5	
Total	

Answers will vary. You have 3 out of 6 chances of drawing a 1, and 1 out of 6 chance of drawing any of the others.

Share

I won ____ out of 3 games.

Is it easier to win or to lose? ________

Play 3 more games. Keep score on the back of this paper. Play with a partner. Which number did you pull most often? ____

FOCUS: Students use number sense to predict the outcome of a set of events.

Name ______________________________ **Logic**

Use with text pages 225–226.

Party Time

What time did each child come to the party? Read the clues. Draw the clock hands to show the arrival times.

Arrival Times		
3:10	3:15	3:20
3:40	3:55	4:05

HINT Cross out each arrival time after you show it on a clock.

Clues

- Chris came first.
- When Kenny came, the minute hand was on 4.
- When Jesse came, the minute hand and the hour hand were very close to each other.
- When Merle came, the minute hand was on 1.
- Mario came 10 minutes before Merle.
- Karla came 20 minutes after Kenny did.

Kenny Merle Chris

 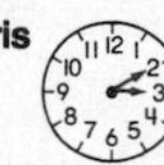 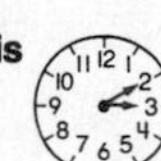

Jesse Mario Karla

 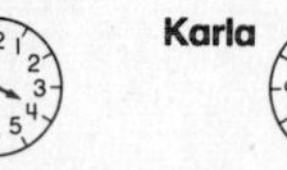

FOCUS: Students use their knowledge of time and deductive reasoning to solve a logic puzzle.

Name ______________________________ **Decision Making**

Use with text pages 227–228.

In What Order?

Jason has these things to do this afternoon. Show the order in which he should do them. Number them from 1 to 5.

Answers may vary.

1 Sign up for dodgeball at the playground between 1:30 and 3:30.

2 Watch boat race at pond between 2:30 and 3:30.

4 Pick up bike at Fix-It Shop before 5:00.

3 Jeff is going to camp tonight. See him before 4:30.

5 Buy milk for dinner. The Corner Store closes at 6:00.

Now draw a line on the map to show his path. Number the stops.

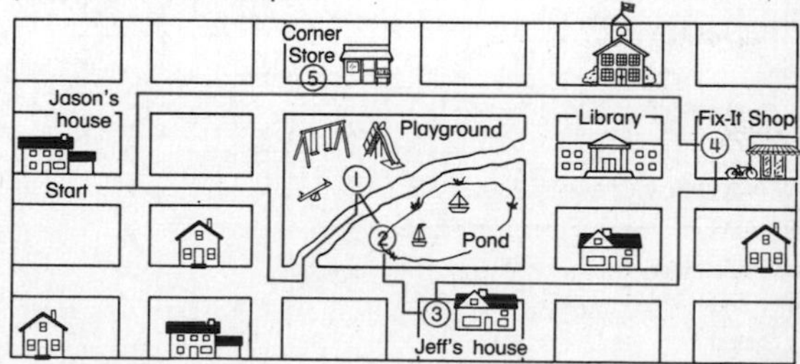

FOCUS: Students order a list of tasks with time constraints and then mark a map to show that order.

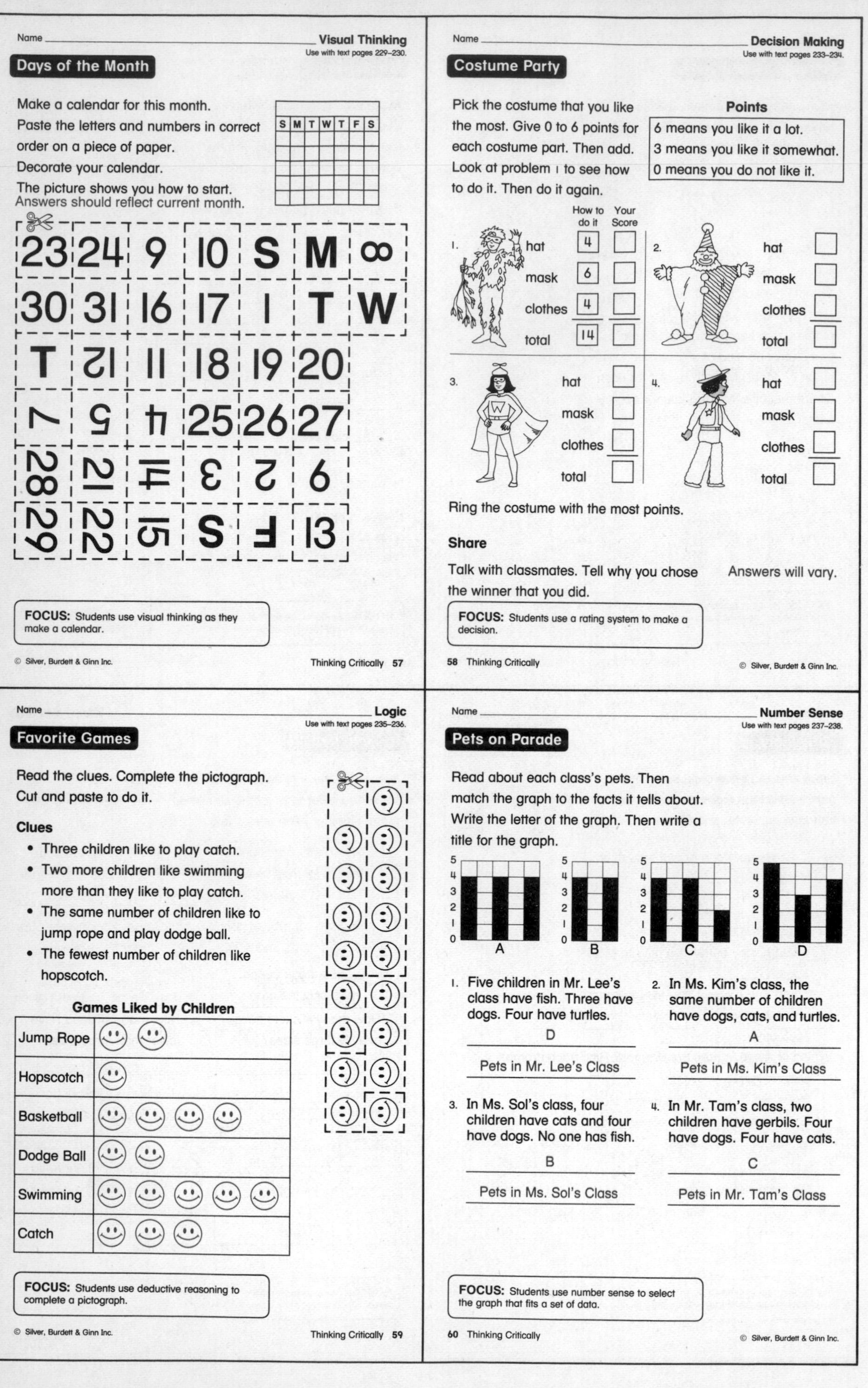

Name ______________________ **Visual Thinking**
Use with text pages 229–230.

Days of the Month

Make a calendar for this month.
Paste the letters and numbers in correct order on a piece of paper.
Decorate your calendar.
The picture shows you how to start.
Answers should reflect current month.

S	M	T	W	T	F	S

FOCUS: Students use visual thinking as they make a calendar.

Name ______________________ **Decision Making**
Use with text pages 233–234.

Costume Party

Pick the costume that you like the most. Give 0 to 6 points for each costume part. Then add. Look at problem 1 to see how to do it. Then do it again.

Points

6 means you like it a lot.
3 means you like it somewhat.
0 means you do not like it.

1.

	How to do it	Your Score
hat	4	
mask	6	
clothes	4	
total	14	

2. hat ☐ mask ☐ clothes ☐ total ☐

3. hat ☐ mask ☐ clothes ☐ total ☐

4. hat ☐ mask ☐ clothes ☐ total ☐

Ring the costume with the most points.

Share

Talk with classmates. Tell why you chose the winner that you did. Answers will vary.

FOCUS: Students use a rating system to make a decision.

Name ______________________ **Logic**
Use with text pages 235–236.

Favorite Games

Read the clues. Complete the pictograph.
Cut and paste to do it.

Clues

- Three children like to play catch.
- Two more children like swimming more than they like to play catch.
- The same number of children like to jump rope and play dodge ball.
- The fewest number of children like hopscotch.

Games Liked by Children

Jump Rope	☺ ☺
Hopscotch	☺
Basketball	☺ ☺ ☺ ☺
Dodge Ball	☺ ☺
Swimming	☺ ☺ ☺ ☺ ☺
Catch	☺ ☺ ☺

FOCUS: Students use deductive reasoning to complete a pictograph.

Name ______________________ **Number Sense**
Use with text pages 237–238.

Pets on Parade

Read about each class's pets. Then match the graph to the facts it tells about. Write the letter of the graph. Then write a title for the graph.

1. Five children in Mr. Lee's class have fish. Three have dogs. Four have turtles.
   D
   Pets in Mr. Lee's Class

2. In Ms. Kim's class, the same number of children have dogs, cats, and turtles.
   A
   Pets in Ms. Kim's Class

3. In Ms. Sol's class, four children have cats and four have dogs. No one has fish.
   B
   Pets in Ms. Sol's Class

4. In Mr. Tam's class, two children have gerbils. Four have dogs. Four have cats.
   C
   Pets in Mr. Tam's Class

FOCUS: Students use number sense to select the graph that fits a set of data.

Name ________________ **Visual Thinking**
Use with text pages 249–250.

Shapes Around Us

Many objects around us look like these shapes. We can see these shapes in buildings. We see them in many things that we have in our homes and in schools.

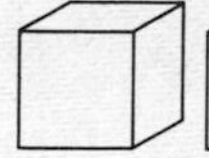 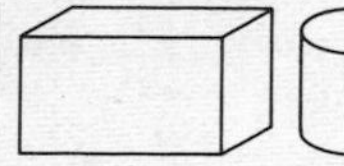 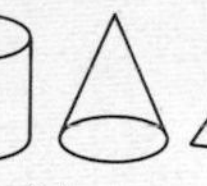 

Find some magazines with many pictures. Find pictures of objects that look something like the shapes. Sometimes an object will show two or more shapes. Cut out the pictures and sort them. Paste pictures that show one kind of shape on a large sheet of paper. Make a poster for each different shape. Make a title for each poster.

Share

Posters may vary.

Share your posters with all of your classmates. Did you choose pictures of the same objects?

FOCUS: Students use their visual sense to identify objects that have the shape of cubes, cones, cylinders, rectangular prisms, spheres, and pyramids.

Have available old magazines that contain many pictures, large poster paper, paste and markers.

Name ________________ **Visual Thinking**
Use with text pages 251–252.

Construction Workers

Write how many straws and clay balls you will need to build each figure. Then build one of the figures.

Note: You will need nonhardening clay and plastic drinking straws. If you wish, cut straws in half.

1. 6 straws
   4 clay balls

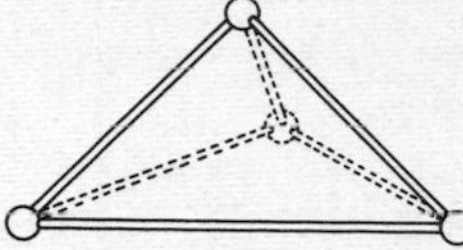

2. 20 straws
   12 clay balls

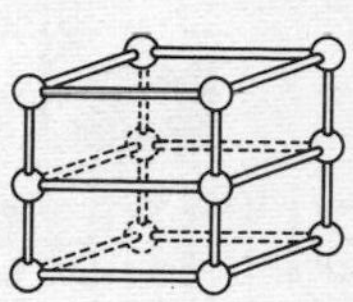

3. 9 straws
   6 clay balls

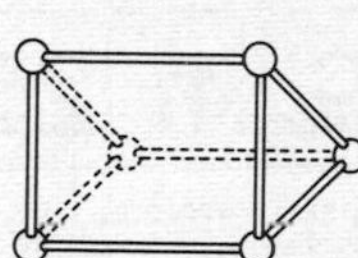

Create Your Own

Construct your own figure. Use 8 clay balls and 12 straws.

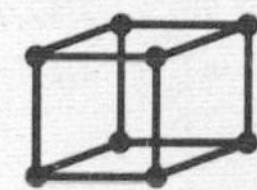

FOCUS: Students use their knowledge of spatial relationships to reproduce geometric figures.

Answers may vary. A possible answer is given.

Name ________________ **Relationships**
Use with text pages 253–254.

Clay Figures

Ketti makes clay figures.
Her favorite kind is a *dromo*.

HINT Decide how all dromos are alike.

Each of these figures is a dromo.

None of these figures is a dromo.

  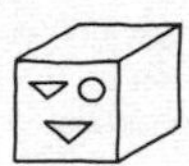

Which of these figures are dromos? Ring each dromo.

1. 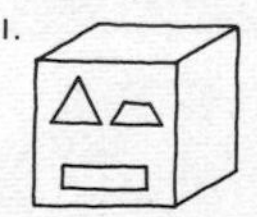 2. 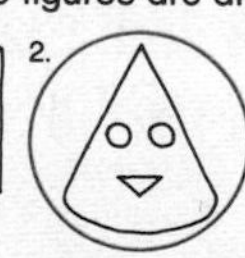 3.  4. 

5. Choose a partner. Compare answers. Talk about what makes a figure a dromo.
   A dromo has two "eyes" that are the same shape and size.
   It has a "mouth" that is a different shape.

FOCUS: Students analyze figures and identify why certain figures fit into a particular group.

Name ________________ **Problem Solving**
Use with text pages 255–256.

Stick to It!

The graph shows how many different stickers Paula has. Use the graph to help you solve each problem. Write the letter A, B, C, or D to tell how how you solved it.

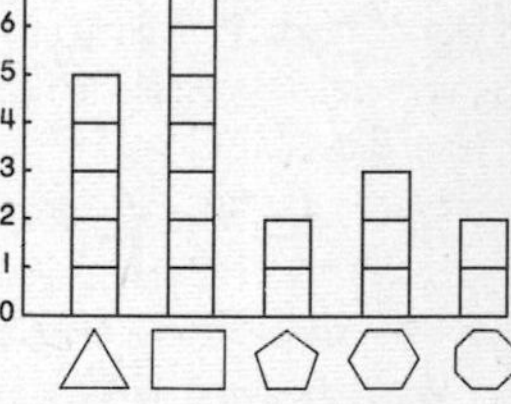

How I Solved the Problem
A. I counted.
B. I added.
C. I counted and added.
D. I read only the graph.

Methods may vary. Possible methods are given.

1. How many stickers have exactly three sides? 5, D
2. How many stickers have more than five sides? 5, A
3. How many stickers have fewer than six sides? 14, A or B
4. How many stickers have fewer than three sides? 0, D
5. How many stickers have four sides or more? 14, A or C
6. How many stickers have more than eight sides? 0, D
7. Paula has 19, C or A stickers altogether.

FOCUS: Students solve problems based on data given in a graph and identify the methods that they used.

Name ____________________ **Logic**
Use with text pages 265–266.

Sorting Flags

Complete the chart below.
Use tally marks and numbers.

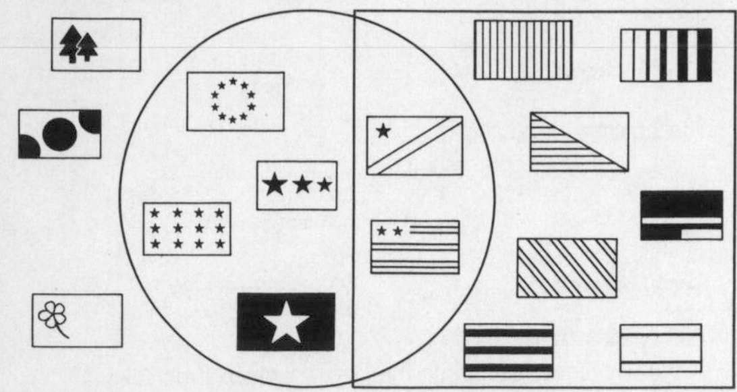

Places for Flags	Tally	Number
Flags in the circle	~~||||~~ I	6
Flags in the square	~~||||~~ IIII	9
Flags in both the circle and the square	II	2
Flags not in the circle or the square	III	3
Flags in all	~~||||~~ ~~||||~~ ~~||||~~ I	16

FOCUS: Students use logic to interpret a Venn diagram.

Name ____________________ **Logic**
Use with text pages 267–268.

Fly a Kite

The kites are tangled up. Help the frogs find their kites.

Use the clues. Ring the correct kite.

1. My kite is round. $\frac{2}{3}$ of it is black.

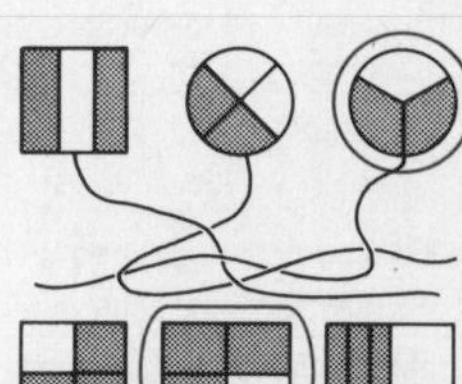

2. My kite is not square. $\frac{3}{4}$ of it is black.

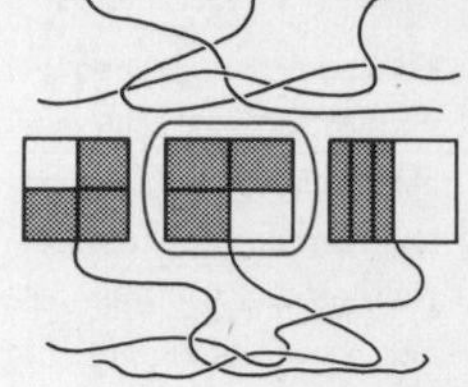

3. My kite is not a triangle. The black part is not $\frac{1}{4}$ of it.

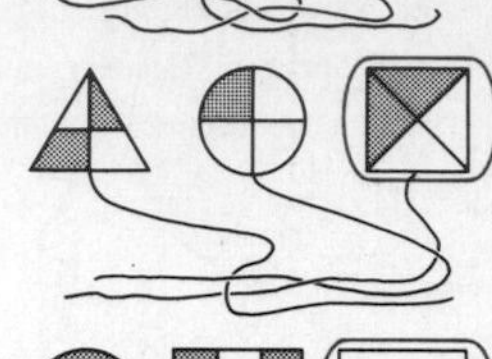

4. My kite is not square. It is not round. The black part is not $\frac{2}{3}$ of it.

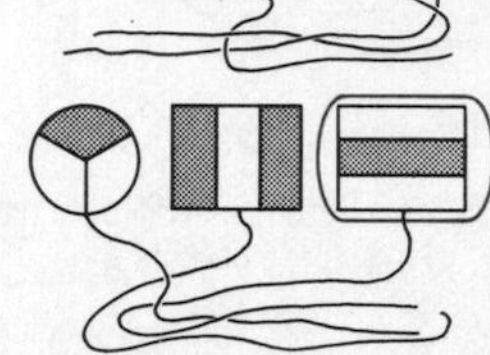

FOCUS: Students use deductive reasoning to identify the object described.

Name ____________________ **Number Sense**
Use with text pages 269–270.

Rhyme Time

Each problem tells about a part of a group of things. Find each answer. Draw pictures or use counters to help you.

1. Rub-a-dub dub.
 16 birds in a tub.
 $\frac{1}{2}$ of them fly away.
 How many birds fly away?
 8

2. Hickory dickory dock.
 12 mice on a clock.
 $\frac{1}{4}$ of them run away.
 How many mice run away?
 3

3. Hey diddle diddle.
 12 ants on a fiddle.
 $\frac{1}{3}$ of them crawl off.
 How many ants crawl off?
 4

4. Little Miss Tuppets
 had 14 puppets.
 $\frac{1}{2}$ of them were broken.
 How many puppets were broken?
 7

Ring the best estimate for this problem.

5. Old King Nolls
 Made 36 rolls.
 $\frac{1}{2}$ of the rolls were sold.
 How many rolls are left?
 (more than 10) less than 10

FOCUS: Students use manipulatives or drawings and number sense to solve problems involving parts of a group.

Name ____________________ **Visual Thinking**
Use with text pages 271–272.

Making Pizza Pies

Cut out the pieces of pie. Paste them on the circles to show whole pies.

For these pies, the parts of each pie must all be the same size.

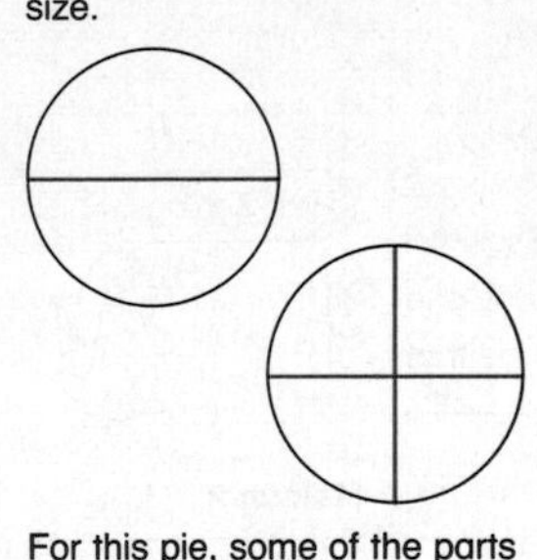

For this pie, some of the parts must be of a different shape and size. Be sure you make exactly one whole pie.

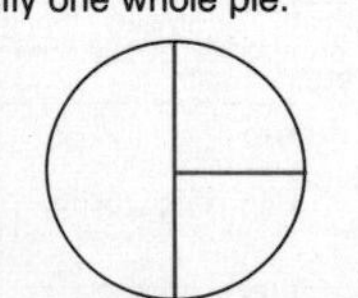

Pieces to Cut

Cut along the broken lines. You will not use all of the pieces.

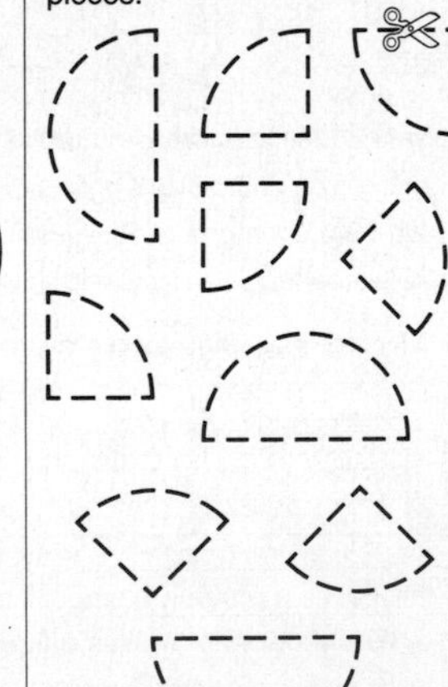

FOCUS: Students use manipulatives to show that $\frac{2}{2}$ = 1 and that one whole can be made with parts of the same size or with parts that are not all the same size.

Name ______________________ **Number Sense**
Use with text pages 273–274.

Spin the Spinner

Color the part where the spinner would stop more times.

1. 2. 3.

Color the part where the spinner would stop fewer times.

4. 5. 6.

Create Your Own

Draw a spinner with two parts. Number the parts 1 and 2. Make the spinner so that it will stop more times on part 1.

FOCUS: Students determine the probability of an event by marking a part of a circle.

Name ______________________ **Number Sense**
Use with text pages 275–276.

Some Sums

Karen made these five number cards. She put them in a bag and picked these two. Is the sum less than 25 or greater than 25?

8 | 12 | 16 | 20 | 24

12 | 16

Write *greater* or *less*. greater

Copy the set of number cards. Put the cards into a bag and pick two. Is the sum less than 25 or greater than 25? Write a tally mark in the correct place on the chart. Pick two cards and add them. Put the two cards back into the bag. Do this ten times. Which did you get more often? Ring your answer.

Less than 25	
More than 25	

a sum less than 25

a sum greater than 25

A sum greater than 25 is more likely.

Share

Compare your results with those of a classmate. Were they similar? Why?

Answers may vary. There are more pairs of numbers that have sums greater than 25 than pairs that have sums less than 25.

FOCUS: Students use number sense to analyze a probability situation.

Name ______________________ **Decision Making**
Use with text pages 277–278.

Eating Out

Lunch Menu

ABC soup	25¢	grape juice	8¢	apple	9¢
pizza	35¢	milk	17¢	peach	7¢
burger	30¢	orange juice	14¢	yogurt	12¢

Decisions may vary. Lead a discussion about decisions.

You have 80¢. You want to have at least 20¢ left after you pay for lunch. Show two lunches you could buy if you choose one thing from each group. Ring the one that you like better.

Pick 3 things.

Lunch 1	Lunch 2
ABC soup	burger
grape juice	milk
yogurt	peach
Total—45¢; 35¢ left	Total—54¢; 26¢ left

FOCUS: Students use personal judgments and computational skills to help make decisions.

Name ______________________ **Number Sense**
Use with text pages 289–290.

Perry's Perimeters

Perry found some grid paper. Each small square is 1 centimeter on each side. Perry drew this rectangle. What is the perimeter?

The perimeter is 8 centimeters.

Use the grids below. Try to draw a rectangle with the given perimeter. If you can draw it, ring *yes*. If you can't, ring *no*. Draw only on the grid lines.

1. 12 centimeters (yes) no
2. 16 centimeters (yes) no
3. 11 centimeters yes (no)

No. 5

4. 17 centimeters yes (no)

5. Draw a green rectangle with a perimeter of 10 centimeters. Use one of the grids above.

FOCUS: Students use their number sense to analyze and draw rectangles with given perimeters.

Name ______ **Number Sense**
Use with text pages 295–296.

Weigh-In

These are coins from the Planet Star. Each one has a different weight.

⊗ 1 gram   ▽ 5 grams   ⬡ 10 grams

Answer each question.

1. How much does 1 ⬡, 1 ▽, and 7 ⊗ weigh? 22 grams.
2. Could you make a pile that weighs the same number of grams with fewer coins? Show how by writing the missing numbers.
   1 ⬡, 2 ▽, 2 ⊗
3. Make each of these amounts. Try to use the *fewest* number of coins possible.
   Answers may vary. Possible answers are given.

4. 7 grams — 1 ▽, 2 ⊗
5. 15 grams — 1 ⬡, 1 ▽
6. 24 grams — 2 ⬡, 4 ⊗
7. 35 grams — 3 ⬡, 1 ▽
8. 41 grams — 4 ⬡, 1 ⊗
9. 49 grams — 4 ⬡, 1 ▽, 4 ⊗

FOCUS: Students use number sense to use the fewest number of weights to make a given number of grams.

Name ______ **Visual Thinking**
Use with text pages 297–298.

Tile Floors

Each white space in this drawing stands for a tile. The black space shows that some tiles are missing. How many tiles are missing? 2

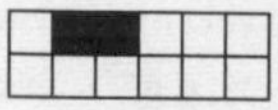

How many tiles are missing in each drawing?

1. 5
2.  6
3. 6
4.  6
5.  16
6.  15
7.  16
8. 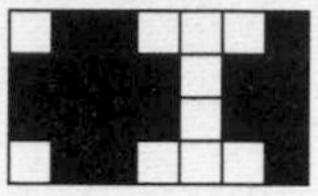 18
9.  12

FOCUS: Students use visual thinking to determine how many squares are missing in a rectangular-shaped grid.

Name ______ **Problem Solving**
Use with text pages 299–300.

Measurement Mix-Up

In each problem some numbers are missing. For the first number, choose from the box a reasonable number that fits the story. Then solve the problem. The answer is not in the box.

23	75	2	$\frac{1}{2}$

HINT Use each number in the box just once.

1. Outside it was cold. At 5 o'clock the temperature was 2 °C. In the next hour the temperature dropped 2 degrees. What was the temperature then? 0 °C
2. The house was gloomy, but it was heated. The temperature was 23 °C. In the next hour it might rise another 4 degrees. What would the temperature be then? 27 °C
3. Carl found a step ladder that was about 10 centimeters taller than his dog Rover. Rover was 75 centimeters tall. How tall was the ladder? 85 centimeters.
4. "Hey, Carl!" Ben said. "Look! I found the two paint cans that we need. Each has $\frac{1}{2}$ liter of paint in it." How much paint in all was in the cans? 1 liter.

FOCUS: Students select reasonable numbers to use as data in problems and then solve the problems.

Name ______ **Logic**
Use with text pages 305–306.

If, Then

Follow each direction before going on to the next one.

HINT You may have to both color *and* ring some objects.

1. • If the shape is a circle, then color it red.
   • If it is not a circle, then ring it. 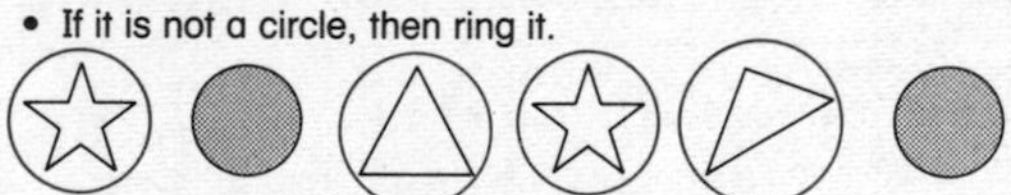
2. • If the shape is a square, then color it blue.
   • If it is not a circle, then ring it.

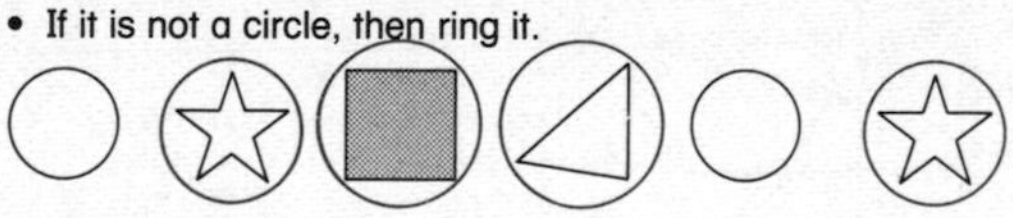

Create Your Own

Complete the sentences for these shapes. Give them to a classmate to solve.

If the shape is a ______ ,

then color it ______ .

If it is not a ______ , then ring it.

Answers will vary.

FOCUS: Students use logical thinking to follow *if, then* sentences.

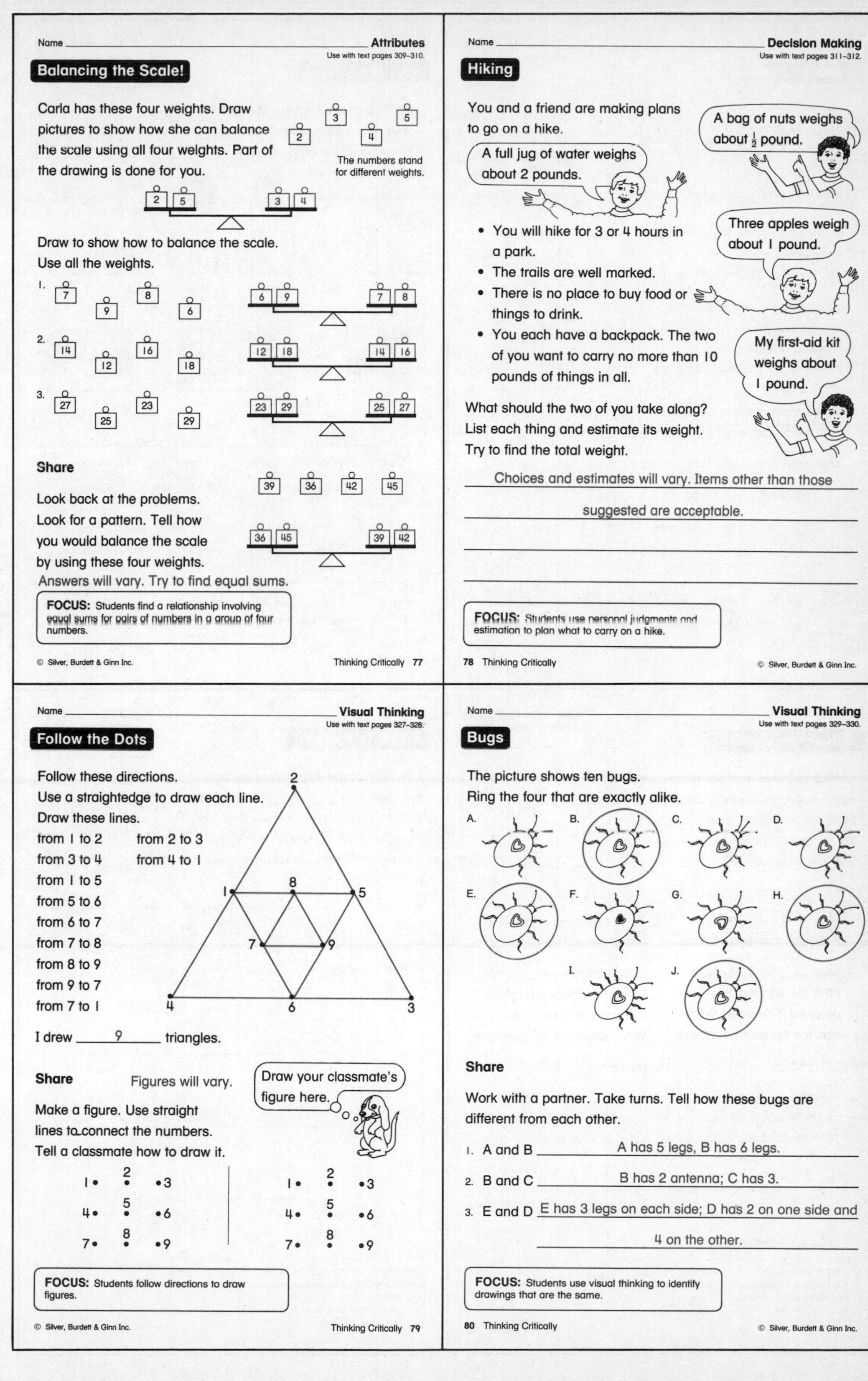

Name ____________________ **Attributes**

Use with text pages 309–310.

Balancing the Scale!

Carla has these four weights. Draw pictures to show how she can balance the scale using all four weights. Part of the drawing is done for you.

2 3 4 5

The numbers stand for different weights.

2 5 | 3 4

Draw to show how to balance the scale. Use all the weights.

1. 7 9 8 6 — 6 9 | 7 8
2. 14 12 16 18 — 12 18 | 14 16
3. 27 25 23 29 — 23 29 | 25 27

Share

Look back at the problems. Look for a pattern. Tell how you would balance the scale by using these four weights.

39 36 42 45 — 36 45 | 39 42

Answers will vary. Try to find equal sums.

FOCUS: Students find a relationship involving equal sums for pairs of numbers in a group of four numbers.

Name ____________________ **Decision Making**

Use with text pages 311–312.

Hiking

You and a friend are making plans to go on a hike.

A bag of nuts weighs about $\frac{1}{2}$ pound.
A full jug of water weighs about 2 pounds.
Three apples weigh about 1 pound.
My first-aid kit weighs about 1 pound.

- You will hike for 3 or 4 hours in a park.
- The trails are well marked.
- There is no place to buy food or things to drink.
- You each have a backpack. The two of you want to carry no more than 10 pounds of things in all.

What should the two of you take along? List each thing and estimate its weight. Try to find the total weight.

Choices and estimates will vary. Items other than those suggested are acceptable.

FOCUS: Students use personal judgments and estimation to plan what to carry on a hike.

Name ____________________ **Visual Thinking**

Use with text pages 327–328.

Follow the Dots

Follow these directions.
Use a straightedge to draw each line.
Draw these lines.

from 1 to 2 from 2 to 3
from 3 to 4 from 4 to 1
from 1 to 5
from 5 to 6
from 6 to 7
from 7 to 8
from 8 to 9
from 9 to 7
from 7 to 1

I drew 9 triangles.

Share Figures will vary.

Make a figure. Use straight lines to connect the numbers. Tell a classmate how to draw it.

Draw your classmate's figure here.

FOCUS: Students follow directions to draw figures.

Name ____________________ **Visual Thinking**

Use with text pages 329–330.

Bugs

The picture shows ten bugs.
Ring the four that are exactly alike.

Share

Work with a partner. Take turns. Tell how these bugs are different from each other.

1. A and B A has 5 legs, B has 6 legs.
2. B and C B has 2 antenna; C has 3.
3. E and D E has 3 legs on each side; D has 2 on one side and 4 on the other.

FOCUS: Students use visual thinking to identify drawings that are the same.

Name ______________________ **Logic**
Use with text pages 333–334.

Animal Parade

Beaver	Ostrich	Tiger	Giant Panda	Lion	Eagle
65 pounds	300 pounds	600 pounds	350 pounds	550 pounds	14 pounds

Use the picture and the information.
Complete each statement. Answers will vary.

1. All of the animals weigh more than 13 pounds, but less than 601 pounds.
2. Some of the animals have 4 legs and fur and some have 2 legs and feathers.
3. None of the animals weigh more than 600 pounds or less than 14 pounds.
4. Some of the animals have names that begin with the letters *b, t,* and *l.*

FOCUS: Students use logical thinking to complete statements involving all, some, and none.

Name ______________________ **Problem Solving**
Use with text pages 335–336.

Rock Collections

The children are carrying rocks in the boxes. The numbers tell how many rocks are in each box.

Luanne	Paul	Tony	Marla	Julie	Ben
18, 25	15	19, 23	32	101	13

Read and solve each problem.

1. How many rocks is Tony carrying?
   42 rocks
2. Who is carrying the fewest rocks?
   Ben
3. How many more rocks is Marla carrying than Paul?
   17 rocks
4. Which children are carrying more than 40 rocks?
   Luanne, Tony, Julie
5. Which problems did you solve by adding?
   1, 4
6. Which problem did you solve by subtracting?
   3

FOCUS: Students solve problems and identify the number operation used.

Name ______________________ **Visual Thinking/Project**
Use with text pages 339–340.

Bigger and Bigger

Here is a drawing on grid paper. You can make a larger drawing like it. You can copy it on the grid below. Each square is larger than a square on the smaller drawing, so your drawing will be larger.

Work with a partner. Talk about making the larger picture. Talk about where the sun and clouds are in your larger picture. Each of you can make part of the picture, or each of you can do the whole picture.

FOCUS: Students use visual thinking, planning, and estimating to enlarge a picture.

Name ______________________ **Visual Thinking/Project**
Use with text pages 339–340.

Bigger and Bigger

You can make a drawing of your own and then enlarge it. Plan a picture with a partner. Draw it on the small grid at the right. Then draw it on the larger grid below. When you have finished, color your picture.

Drawings will vary.

FOCUS: Students use visual thinking and measurement skills to make and then enlarge a picture.

Name ______________________ **Attributes**

Use with text pages 349–350.

Follow Those Arrows!

Maria made this number chart. Then she said, "I see a pattern on this chart. If I start at any number and move 1 space up, it's like adding 25."

Row 1	100	105	110	115	120
	75	80	85	90	95
	50	55	60	65	70
	25	30	35	40	45
	0	5	10	15	20

Maria wrote 5↑ = 30
20↑ = 45

1. Check Maria's pattern. Start with any number in the fourth row. Move 1 space up. Does the result fit Maria's pattern?

   25↑ = 50 30↑ = 55 40↑ = 65

2. If Maria moves 1 space to the right, it is like adding 5. Test the pattern.

   5→ = 10 10→ = 15 35→ = 40

3. Study these patterns. Test them.

   0↗ = 30 10↗ = 40 55↗ = 85 40↗ = 70

   0↗→ = 35 10↗→ = 45 55↗→ = 90 50↗→ = 85

   25↗→ = 60 35↗→ = 70 30↗→ = 65

FOCUS: Students discover patterns by making moves on a number chart.

Name ______________________ **Visual Thinking**

Use with text pages 353–354.

Butterfly Net

Cut out the large square piece of paper. Fold it in half. Cut the folded paper to make the design. Then paste your cutout on another piece of paper. Color it.

Here's how I made this shape.

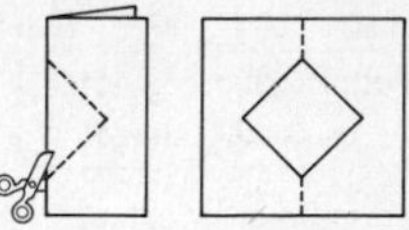

Designs will vary.

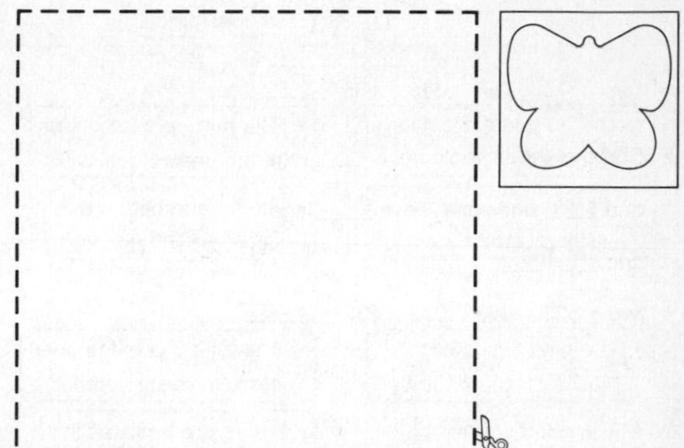

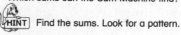

FOCUS: Students use mental imagery to create a design.

Name ______________________ **Number Sense**

Use with text pages 355–356.

Alphabet Soup

Some letters are vowels. Some are consonants. Cut out the letters below. Place them in a bag. **What if** you pick 10 of them? Which type of letter will you pick more often?

Vowels
A, E, I, O, U

Consonants
B, C, D, F, G, H, J, K, L, M, N, P, Q, R, S, T, V, W, X, Y, Z

Ring your guess.

more vowels more consonants

Now pick 10 letters. Write them in the spaces where they belong. Answers may vary

Type	Letters	Total
Vowels		
Consonants		

I drew more consonants.

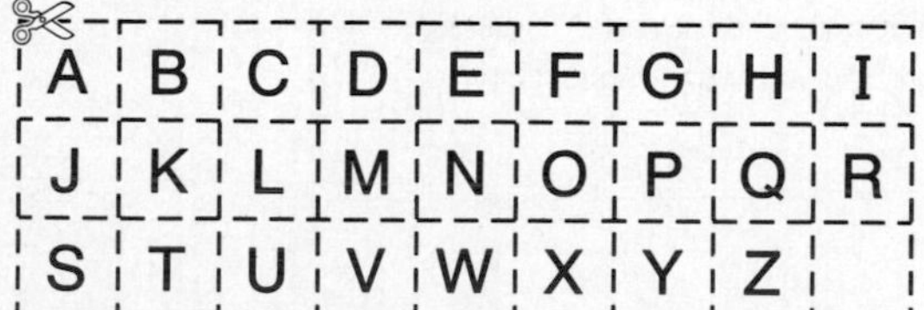

FOCUS: Students predict the probability of an event and show the results in an experiment.

Name ______________________ **Logic**

Use with text pages 357–358.

Sum Machine!

Which sums can the Sum Machine find?

Find the sums. Look for a pattern.

The Sum Machine will find the sum of these problems.

$128 + 427 = 555$ $201 + 132 = 333$ $864 + 135 = 999$ $172 + 50 = 222$

It will not find these sums.

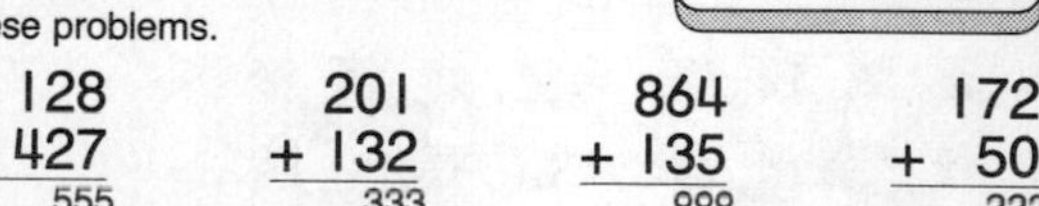

$507 + 215 = 722$ $342 + 469 = 811$ $110 + 87 = 197$ $289 + 605 = 894$

Ring the problems that the Sum Machine will add.

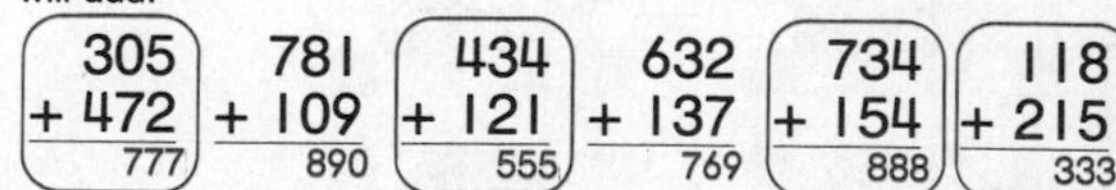

$305 + 472 = 777$ $781 + 109 = 890$ $434 + 121 = 555$ $632 + 137 = 769$ $734 + 154 = 888$ $118 + 215 = 333$

Create Your Own

Write two different problems that the Sum Machine will solve.

FOCUS: Students use logical reasoning to find a pattern and use it to identify and write problems that follow the pattern.

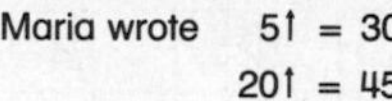

Name ______________________ **Attributes**
Use with text pages 359–360.

Grouping Numbers

Study each group of numbers. Ring each sentence that describes the numbers. Then write another number that fits the group.

Answers will vary.

1. 235 150 105 175 355 300
   - The numbers are greater than 100 and less than 400.
   - The numbers all have 5 in ones place.
   - The numbers are all odd numbers.
   - If I add any two of them, the sum will have 0 or 5 in ones place.

2. 166 376 264 346 136 ____
   - The numbers are all even numbers.
   - The numbers have 4 or 6 in the ones place.
   - We say these numbers if we skip count by 2.
   - All the numbers are between 150 and 400.

3. 363 633 533 343 233 ____
   - The digit 3 is in two places in every number.
   - The digit 3 is in the ones place in every number.
   - The numbers are all greater than 100 and less than 600.
   - There are 3 places in each number.

FOCUS: Students identify attributes of a group of numbers and write a number that has the same attributes.

Name ______________________ **Number Sense**
Use with text pages 363–364.

Cora's Cross-Number Puzzle

Cora wrote a cross-number puzzle. It gives some of the answers and some of the clues. Write the rest of the answers and clues.

Answers will vary. Possible answers for clues are given.

		A 1	5	B 2		C 9	6	D 1		E 3	8	F 6
G 2	3	8		H 5	7	0		I 2	1	4		7

Across

A. The next number after 151
C. The next number after 960
E. 300 + 80 + 6
G. 2 hundreds 3 tens 8 ones
H. 5 hundreds 7 tens
I. 200 + 14; 100 + 114

Down

A. 9 + 9
B. 35 – 10
C. 95 – 5
D. 9 + 3
E. 30 + 4; 3 tens 4 ones
F. 60 + 7; 6 tens 4 ones

FOCUS: Students use number sense to respond correctly to clues and to write clues for a cross-number puzzle.

Name ______________________ **Visual Thinking**
Use with text pages 367–368.

Square Deal

Copy the design. Color only the squares that should be shaded.

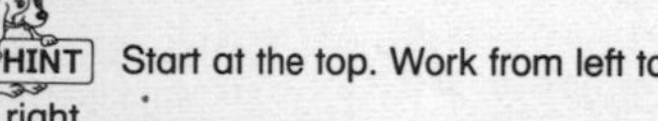

Start at the top. Work from left to right.

1.
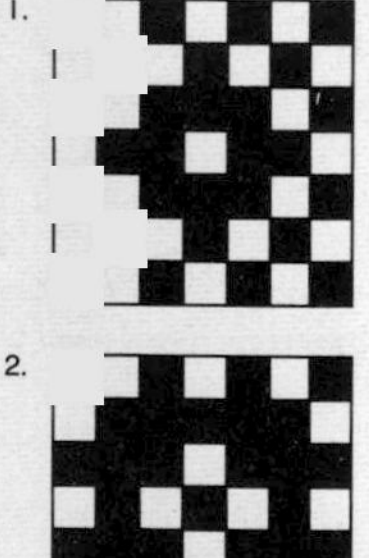

2.

3.

FOCUS: Students use visual imagery to copy a design onto a grid.

Name ______________________ **Number Sense**
Use with text pages 369–370.

Sixty-eight's

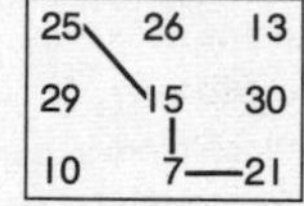

Answers may vary. Possible answers are given.

Make one path in each box. The numbers on the path should have a sum of exactly 68. Numbers must be joined by straight lines. You may use a calculator or paper and pencil to help you.

1.
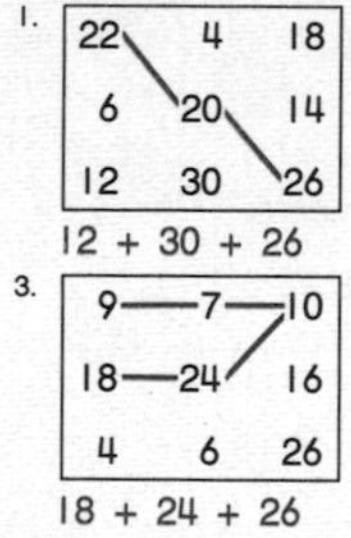

12 + 30 + 26

2.
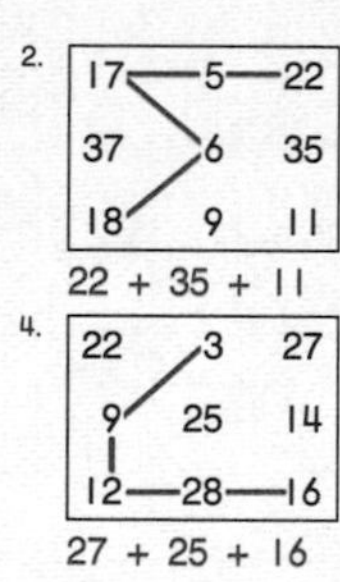

22 + 35 + 11

3.
9 7 10
18 24 16
4 6 26

18 + 24 + 26

4.
22 3 27
9 25 14
12 28 16

27 + 25 + 16

Work Space

25
+ 15
40

Share

Compare your work with a classmate's work. Did you find the same paths?

FOCUS: Students use number sense to solve a number search puzzle.

Name ______________________ **Number Sense**
Use with text pages 385–386.

Parts Make a Whole

How many grid boxes will each shape cover? Guess. Then cut out the shapes and count the squares.

1\.

2\.

Answers will vary.

1. Cover boxes with △.
Guess ____________
Count 12½

2. Cover boxes with ○.
Guess ____________
Count about 29

Share

Tell how you counted parts of grid boxes.

FOCUS: Students estimate area and check their estimates.

Name ______________________ **Decision Making**
Use with text pages 371–372.

Trip Time

You are traveling from Avon to Lyle.

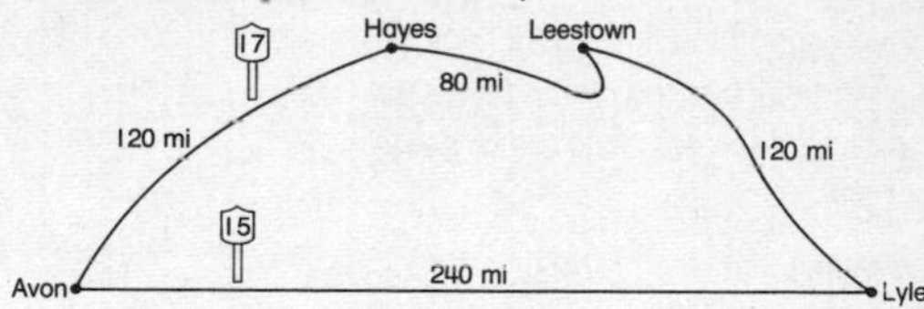

Use the map to solve these problems.

1. You went from Avon to Leestown in one day. How many miles did you travel?
200 miles

2. The second day you went from Leestown to Lyle. How long was that trip?
120 miles

3. What is the total number of miles between Avon and Lyle on Route 17?
320 miles

4. How long is the trip from Avon to Lyle if you travel on Route 15?
240 miles

5. How much longer is the trip from Avon to Lyle if you travel on Route 17 than if you travel on Route 15?
80 miles

6. **What if** Route 15 and Route 17 were both good roads? Which one would you travel? Explain.
Answers will vary.

FOCUS: Students use computational skills to solve problems and thinking skills to form an opinion.

Name ______________________ **Relationships**
Use with text pages 387–388.

Look Alikes

Look at the numbers in each star. Decide how they are alike. Write another number that belongs to the group.

Answers will vary.

111 777 888 999 333 222 — 444 555 666

All three digits are the same.

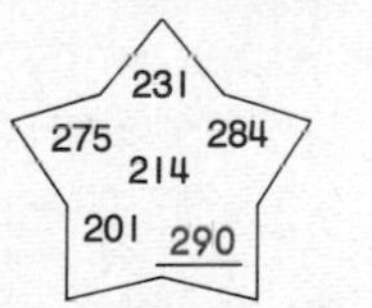

2 is in the hundreds place.

Make two groups of your own. Use these numbers.

12 35 45 18
16 65 14 85

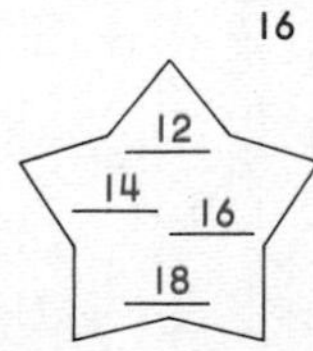

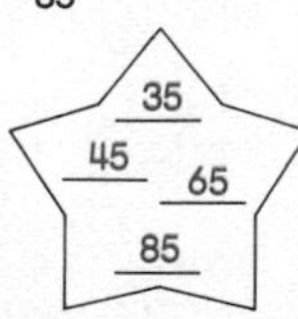

Share

Ask a classmate to give a rule that describes each of your groups and then add a number to each group.

FOCUS: Students determine the relationship that exists among numbers in a group.

Name ______________________ **Problem Solving**
Use with text pages 393–394.

Watch the Birdy

The Bird Club members looked for robins and owls. Ring the questions that you can answer by using the chart. Then find the answer. Write *cannot tell* for the questions you cannot answer.

	Robins	Owls
Monday	7	22
Tuesday	16	15
Wednesday	3	4

1. How many robins did they see in all? 26

2. How many owls did they see in all? 41

3. On Thursday, did they see more robins or more owls?
cannot tell

4. On Tuesday, did they see more robins or more owls.?
more robins

5. On which day did they see the most birds?
Tuesday

6. How many birds did they see in one week?
cannot tell

7. What do you need to know to solve the problems that you cannot answer?
For 2, how many birds that they saw on the other 4 days;
For 3, how many birds that they saw on Thursday

FOCUS: Students determine whether or not there is enough information to solve problems and tell what information is missing.

Name ______________________ **Decision Making**
Use with text pages 395–396.

Free Time

You have exactly 60 minutes free. How would you spend the time? Write what you would do. Write the starting time for each activity. Pick five activities or some of your own.

Riding my bike	Playing tic-tac-toe	Drawing
Doing cartwheels	Seeing a puppet show	Reading
Writing a letter	Playing catch	
Going to the movies	Visiting the zoo	

My Plan

1:00 ______________________

___ : ___ ______________________

___ : ___ ______________________

___ : ___ ______________________

___ : ___ ______________________

Answers will vary. Lead a discussion about students' plans.

FOCUS: Students use their knowledge of time to decide on a schedule.

B C D E F G H I J—PO—96 95 94 93 92 91